THE GRASSHOPPERS COME
AND
A RABBIT IN THE AIR

The Grasshoppers Come

AND

A Rabbit in the Air

DAVID GARNETT

ILLUSTRATED WITH
WOOD ENGRAVINGS AND DRAWINGS
BY
R. A. GARNETT

faber and faber

This edition first published in 2009
by Faber and Faber Ltd
Bloomsbury House, 74–77 Great Russell Street
London WC1B 3DA

A CIP record for this book is available from the British Library

ISBN 978-0-571-25377-7

THE
GRASSHOPPERS COME

WOOD ENGRAVINGS BY R. A. GARNETT

Flying locust . . . . title-page

The Pe-shan . . . . . p. 45

The bird . . . . . . p. 71

The fire . . . . . . p. 91

The Chinese Moth . . . . p. 97

Locusts hatching . . . . p. 101

THE GRASSHOPPERS

COME

THERE was a withered yellow tip to every reed so that each one was partly dead even though it was still growing, and these yellow tips made an autumnal landscape in the heat of June. When a breath of wind came to bend them down, the reeds at one moment were all yellow, and then, as they stooped lower under the caress, grey-green.

They grew in the soft clay along the river for a hundred miles, in beds that were a mile across on each side, so that the river was lost in them and no man or beast in that empty land of the tundras could approach it.

Overhead the sun shone in a cloudless sky. You might ride all day and the day after before you came to men or cattle; but in the river the sturgeon swam and in the reeds a few unmated storks still lingered sadly. All day long the bed of reeds was filled with a sound which was so monotonous and unceasing that, like the heat of the sun and the blueness of the sky and the yellow tips of the reeds, it determined the character of the place itself.

This sound was the stridulation of grasshoppers, or locusts, gathered into a choir so vast that the chirrup of individuals was not noticeable: the sound was not altered perceptibly when the nearest of them fell silent. Sometimes one of the musicians would crawl higher than usual on a reed, right up to the yellow tip, and after clinging there and stridulating, would spread out his flat wing-cases, and with a whirr of gauzy underwings and a big jump, would fly off aimlessly and after a few yards flop so heavily among the reeds that it was a wonder that his brittle joints were not broken. Sometimes, however, they were, and the maimed creature would sink lower and lower down among the reeds and disappear.

Each day as the sun sank the grasshoppers would climb up the reeds until the yellow tips were thick with insects, and when it set, with millions of little horny eyes they gazed at the vanishing rim, and then, clinging tighter, they swayed with the reeds throughout the night, motionless until dawn broke and drew their eyes to the east, to catch sight of the first flames.

In the twilight and before the dawn the rare storks moved like pale ghosts among the reeds, busily employed with their long sword-shaped bills among the frozen sun-worshippers.

But each day as the sun grew hotter with the advance of summer, more and more grasshoppers would open their wings and launch themselves into the air and, with many blind collisions, would rise higher in little whirling eddies that drifted with the wind over the tops of the reeds before they sank down again. Often, when a little bunch of four or five fell clumsily together in one spot, it would startle an insect that had been stridulating there into a short outlying flight, so that, when one of these incipient swarms subsided and pattered down among the reeds, it threw up a few more flying insects like splashes of mud on a dirty road.

As each day of the early summer passed, the sun grew hotter, the fine windless weather more settled, and the stridulation noisier, more incessant, and the little whirlpools, which seemed to catch up the flying insects over the reeds, larger and more powerful, holding them up longer in flight.

❁

The green of the great field was vivid. About it, on two sides, were fringes of low oak trees the leaves of which still had a tawny tinge in them as though they had been chapped with chilblains by the late frosts of May. Facing the oak trees were rows of corrugated iron sheds with asphalt in front of each running down into the vivid grass, and the long arms and pipes of giant scarlet or yellow petrol pumps stood beside their huge doorways like etiolated sentries mounting guard.

The fourth side of the great field was bounded by a low wire fence, with a row of newly built, red-tiled little houses on the far side of a black main road. Not far off the electric trams started, for the huge field was on the outskirts of a big town.

From a mast over the Tudor Cottage Club-house, and from four other lower ones set in the middle of

each of the four sides of the field there streamed
tubular banners which were blown out by the
summer wind.

The air was full of sound. Through all the hours
while daylight lasted, now near, now deafening,
now a mere weary buzzing more remote, there
roared the aero engines and the shuddering tune
of whirling propeller tips. The sky vibrated cease-
lessly with noise that beat down and shattered the
peace of the summer day.

Men in blue or khaki overalls came and went,
moved lazily about the sheds, came out on to the
asphalt and looked up briefly at the sky, while, with
scarcely a pause, the great engines tore in circles
round the aerodrome, lifted a few hundred feet into
the air by the light wood and linen wings they
dragged with them.

There were half a dozen aeroplanes flying at
once for most of the day, painted in different
colours, blue and white, yellow and white, or grey
all over, and marked with different letters. Some of
them were biplanes, some monoplanes, and from
their bodies could be seen sometimes one head and
sometimes two protruding, either side by side or
one behind the other.

Round and round they flew, some higher up
wandering off a little way over the surround-
ing country, others lower down, and these lower
machines were continually shutting off their engines
and gliding almost silently in to land, dropping
their tails as they settled down and bounced upon
the earth, when, after a short run, they stopped

until suddenly the engine was opened up again, and they would roar across the grass into the eye of the wind and fly away.

Every half-hour or so each of these machines would come spluttering noisily, bouncing across the grass, taxying to the sheds, and one of the men in it would unfasten his telephone and climb awkwardly out of the rear cockpit and walk slowly to the club-house. While he was still grinning and unbuckling his helmet, another pupil would be strapping himself into the vacant seat, and an overalled mechanic would lift up the tail and wheel the machine round for it to taxy out to the leeward side of the aerodrome.

Occasionally in the course of the day a strange machine which had come from some distant aerodrome would appear high up and slowly descend, gliding with many turns until it was low enough to make the last low left-hand turn and glide softly over the tops of the squat oak trees, and float lower and lower on to the grass which it would touch gently, running forward for a little, before it taxied to the sheds. A weary man would climb out and walk rather stiffly up to the mechanic who approached him. 'Petrol.'

❋

Wright, the ground engineer at the Swynford Club Aerodrome, and his mate Bill smiled gently over their morning's work. Bill was monkeying with the dynamo of Mr. Sefton's car which was not

charging the battery properly, while Wright was
tracing out the cause of an intermittent miss on the
starboard magneto of a Gipsy engine and was toy-
ing with a pair of feeler gauges. Both of them were
free for a little while from interference and they
worked soberly and happily. Wright never hurried
over his work, and if the Club Secretary or one of
the instructors came in to watch him impatiently,
he would knock off work at once or find himself
another job. As he was a good man with a good
record, they let him alone.

On a busy afternoon, of course, things were very
different. Wright in his long yellow coat would
spend his time running from machine to machine,
to lift the tail of one, to hang desperately on to the
end of a wing, while the machine was skidded round
by a burst of engine, and then stand for a moment
with his long black hair blown up on end, and the
skirt of his yellow dust-coat fluttering in the slip-
stream of the propeller, watching the 'plane lum-
bering off across the grass before he turned to meet
another machine, taxying in after a pupil's solo
flight.

There was always an indelible pencil behind
Wright's ear; he had to sign chits, detach counter-
foils, enter times of departure and hand over re-
ceipts at every moment. The fine summer months,
with their lengthened hours of daylight, were spent
in unceasing work, and he looked forward to the
dark, fog-bound December days as the happiest
time of the year, and the prolonged equinoctial
gales when there was no flying at all were welcome.

When the rain lashed wildly on the window-panes and drummed on the galvanised hangar roofs, he could find opportunities to undertake a big overhaul, but in June there was flying every afternoon and all day on Sunday, so that there was only an hour or two each day when he could stoop over the bench and forget the outside world, whistling plaintively to himself and thinking, not so much with his brain as with his fingers, aided by a score of gauges, dies, calipers and machine tools.

Having traced out the short in the dynamo, Bill drifted slowly by Wright's bench eyeing the dismantled engine.

'Seen the paper, chum?'

A shake of the head answered him.

'A Sidestrand crashed up in Scotland, near Rosyth.'

'That'll be a hell of a mess. The Air Force is having a bad time this spring.'

'Well, what d'you expect?' asked Bill, moving on. 'I'll just have time to change that tail-skid Mr. Sykes was complaining about, before lunch.' Wright nodded and sighed again. The paradise of his dreams, which was filled with aeroplanes in perfect condition that never had to leave the ground, was very far away. He was more afraid of crashes than any of the pilots who went up in the machines, and for ten minutes, after Bill had set to work on the skid, the burnt-out wreckage of the Sidestrand came between Wright and his work. But at last the plaintive whistling, like the pipe of a solitary bullfinch in its cage, began again—a

sign that the ground engineer had lost consciousness of himself and had fallen into a trance over the
ignition system, thinking with his hands.

The telephone bell rang.

'Wreaks speaking. Tell Mrs. Johnson that Mrs.
Beanlands and Commander Shap are coming
down for lunch in the club-house. We have had a
favourable weather report and I am to try and get
her unstuck this afternoon, so have the old bus out,
and fill her up full.'

Wright's hand shook as he put back the receiver.
All his peace was gone, and his appetite for lunch
as well. Mrs. Beanlands' long-distance special
monoplane carried a full load of 1900 gallons of
petrol and had already been nearly wrecked once
by running into the far hedge of an aerodrome.
The big crash Wright was dreading was timed for
that afternoon.

❋

Jimmy Wreaks, the tall one-eyed man with the
scars on his face and hands and the broken nose,
sat on the edge of the little basket-work chair
smiling nervously out of politeness. His smile was
a mistake. It showed a hole where a tooth was
missing in the lower jaw and a long yellow eye-
tooth dropping down from the upper one to fill
the gap, and, after revealing what would better
have been kept hidden, this unfortunate smile came
violently in contact with the tight knot of a scar in
the middle of his cheek and was cut off sharp.

They were sitting over luncheon in the club-house. On Jimmy's right was his employer, Mrs. Beanlands, and facing him Commander Shap who was speaking.

'. . . a toast we must all drink: may we beat the long-distance record!' He rose, lifting his glass of champagne, and Jimmy rose and Mrs. Beanlands rose, flushed and rather pretty.

All three stood in silence, clinked glasses and drank and in silence sat down. The champagne bottle was finished. These three were starting that afternoon in *The Wayzgoose*, a big monoplane built to break the world's record for a long-distance flight. It was their fourth attempt to start. On the first occasion they had run into the far hedge of a smaller aerodrome narrowly escaping total destruction, and on the second and third Wreaks had turned back, once because of fog, once for very little cause that he could explain. But as there was a violent storm in Germany that day they forgave him, though they could hardly give him credit for foretelling it two hours before, on the east coast of England.

After so many false starts it was difficult for them to feel sure that they were really off. Shap might be filling up glasses and saying: 'Here's to better luck next time,' at nine o'clock that night. They did not even feel sure that the newspaper men would turn up to photograph the start of the flight. They were aware that they were becoming figures in an old story. Moreover, who cared about long-distance flights any longer? There had been too many of them.

'Now you must have a Benedictine each and a cigar, or your pipes just as you prefer,' said Mrs. Beanlands. 'It will be your last smoke for ever such a long time. Let that make it especially precious to you. So just take whichever you like best.'

'Er—thank you. I will, please,' said Wreaks, holding out his white-scarred hand to take a half a Corona from the box, reflecting that he was not going to be intimidated because a rich woman made an awful fuss over standing him an extra one and sixpence. However dirty the other parts of Jimmy got with ingrained oil, the terrible white patches on the backs of his hands and wrists remained spotless. They marked the places where his flesh had been burnt away when he had fought his way out of a blazing aeroplane, and then into it again to rescue his observer, in 1917.

Mrs. Beanlands knew his history: of proven heroism greater than that in any legend, of matchless skill, of deathless courage, of incredible escapes. . . . She admired the man and she pitied him, but for some time past she had regretted having engaged him.

When Wilmot Shap had first found Wreaks they had both felt that they were marvellously lucky to have secured him. But the flight had been put off so long, ever since March, and she had got to feel the scars and the smile, the yellow tooth and the patch over the eye, very trying indeed.

It was so tiresome for Wilmot and her to have a man of another class with them. Unfortunately they needed a pilot as well as a navigator. It would have been perfect if she and Wilmot could have gone off alone: she had several times been near suggesting it, but she knew that it would not be reasonable or fair to dear Wilmot to make such a proposal. As it was she could not very well engage another pilot instead of Wreaks. He was well known, and she had signed a tiresome contract with him.

Mrs. Beanlands was a fluffy-haired woman of forty, who had come into great wealth on her husband's death. For ten years she had been a faithful, loving and devoted wife, and suddenly, when she had given up all hope of leading an adventurous life of her own, she had come into her reward. Alfred had died, and six months afterwards she had met Wilmot on the Riviera, at Monte Carlo in fact, and the happiest intimacy, the most marvellous romantic adventure, had come out of that meeting.

Lily Beanlands drained the last drop of her glass of Benedictine, looked at her flushed face in a tiny mirror and, rising up from the table, left the two gentlemen to themselves. They hated each other and had nothing to say, so they just lapped up the last of the Benedictine and smoked their cigars.

Wilmot Shap was very dark with such liquid black eyes, so blue a jaw, such well-brushed black hair, that he looked like a sleek water animal, with a wet black coat, ready to plunge into the stream and vanish quickly without leaving a ripple on the surface. There was something adaptable, sinuous and soft about his personality; it was impossible to think of his glossy fur being rubbed up the wrong way. He was a gambler, he had lived all his life by gambling; he was gambling at that moment.

❀

'See you back sometime in August, I suppose,' said Wright the ground engineer. Wreaks smiled.

'You won't leave us all that time hanging out to dry on the far hedge, will you?' he replied, and without waiting to listen to the answer, he climbed rapidly into the front cockpit and gently pushed the throttle open to its full extent.

The 560 h.p. engine roared so that the earth shook and the hangars seemed to waver like packs of cards in the hands of a skilful shuffler; the blast of the slip-stream tore up grass and dirt and covered the photographers with fragments. An onlooker's hat flew away and crumpled itself up round a petrol pump. All thoughts and images in the minds of the three were cut off short: the very faculty of thinking was suspended by the sound which transformed human consciousness to a tight ball of endurance and all outside it to a jelly. The gross physical vibration of sound shook its way through the protective fibres of leather helmet, beat on the eardrum, and the living brain trembled and shook against the sounding-box of the skull.

Wreaks closed the throttle. Mrs. Beanlands' head drooped forward with relief and then she remembered to look about her and smile brightly. Wreaks waved a gloved hand; mechanics pulled away the

chocks and suddenly the engine roared again, the
'plane moved forward, the tail went up and the
machine rushed forward with them into the wind's
eye.

'It seems queer to be setting out on such a voy-
age, on such a summer afternoon,' Mrs. Beanlands
was thinking at that moment. 'It would be more
natural at night, or very early in the morning.'

For forty seconds Commander Shap sat without
breathing, gripping the side of the fuselage, with
lips parted, teeth clenched, eyes staring. He was
afraid.

His sense impressions were broken into discontinu-
ous drops or globules in the agony of anticipating
a horrible death. Sight, hearing, smell, taste and
touch, all had become intermittent.

Mrs. Beanlands turned to him as the machine
raced over the sward and tapped him on the elbow,
but he did not feel her touch and his staring eyes
never moved. She smiled to herself.

'Dear Wilmot! How deeply he feels the romance
of this adventure. It's such a thrilling moment, if
only we don't have to turn back again.' She was
thinking this in the moments of their greatest
danger.

The 'plane was running very fast, and Wreaks
could feel that a large part of the immense weight
was air-borne. He sat perfectly still, holding the
stick just a little forward, determined that at all
costs he would not let the machine bump hard
after she had once lifted. They had not carried
such a full load on any of the previous trials. Sud-

denly Wreaks knew that the machine was going to fly off and he smiled slightly. Two hundred yards from the hedge he relaxed his slight forward pressure on the stick and at once the machine lifted.

Bump! They touched once and they were off. They cleared the hedge by a yard or two and travelled, roaring as they went, through the air, low down over a big arable field. To the nearest spectators it seemed as though they were going to crash, when they were really gathering speed. Wreaks was looking at the A.S.I. (air-speed indicator) and watching the hand creep down to the right: 90-92-95-100. He caressed the forward edge of the stick, *stroking* it back, and the machine at once gained a little height while the hand of the A.S.I. travelled back rather fast: 100-95-90-85. Without hurrying, he pressed the stick a trifle forward. They would clear the trees which stood between them and the estuary and, once they had crossed the belt of low oaks, the ground sloped away from under them and they gained height relatively.

Shake a tube full of dusty little blobs of mercury and suddenly the film of dust which holds one apart from the other breaks down, and in place of a string of beads you have a silver column. Your necklace of beads has become all one thing, which expands and contracts as one and measures the outside world to a nicety.

Wilmot Shap was smiling; he turned to Lily Beanlands with a laugh. 'We hadn't much to spare, but we are all right now.'

Only one globule of mercury remained separate

for longer than the others before it broke into the silvery river. Shap became aware of an ache in his left hand and let go of the fuselage with stiffened paralysed fingers. The tendons in his wrist were a little strained. All was over: all was well.

They were crossing the mudbanks of the estuary; they were over the water. Wreaks was coaxing the machine gently round in a slow left-hand turn. Soon Shap would glance at the first of his file of maps and would mark a compass bearing.

The sky was blue, the sun shining brightly a little behind them on the right-hand side. When Shap looked over the edge he could see their shadow on the left and rather in front of them running along the gleaming mudbank. It was low tide; a tug was steaming downstream, her wake spread out over the surface like a half-closed fan. In front of them was the large red square of the Swynmouth Haven Hotel standing among trees on a cliff overlooking the sea.

Wreaks looked at the sea in front and the ships dotted about in it, then he glanced at the compass by his left knee and followed the line of the centre of the estuary. He was barely 400 feet over the water and decided not to try and gain any more height. If the engine failed they would drown at whatever height they were, but there was not the slightest reason why a Napier Lion fresh from being vetted by Wright should fail. He lifted his hand to the knob of the throttle and gently slid it back, watching the revolution counter as he did so. When the needle was flickering over the figure 21

(2100 revs. a minute) he was satisfied, and looked out once more at the horizon. Then he turned in his seat and caught Shap's eye.

Though the monoplane had been designed originally as a two-seater, the rear cockpit had been enlarged and room had been made in it for two slightly staggered seats. In the forward left-hand one sat Shap, and looking over his right shoulder was Mrs. Beanlands, who was able, by putting her feet up, to lie very nearly at full length. All the pilot's instruments for flying were of course in the front cockpit. Besides the usual instruments the dash was thick with gadgets: for instance there were no less than four separate thermometers recording temperatures of mixture, oil, water and carburettor.

Wreaks regarded most of these devices with scorn: 'Two carburettor thermometers and no wireless. How's that, eh? And do you know why? Because darling Wilmot couldn't be bothered to learn to use a wireless receiver. But they've made up for that in the front cockpit; the chap who designed that instrument panel didn't know I had got only one eye.'

An elaborate system of speaking-tubes had been installed. One pair of tubes connected the front cockpit with the rear. When Commander Shap or Mrs. Beanlands plugged in their telephone connections they could listen to what Wreaks said and could reply through a common mouthpiece. Mrs. Beanlands had to lean forward a little to reach this.

Since they were both in the same cockpit they

could have made each other hear by shouting, but it would have been very exhausting and would have prevented their conversing on a long flight. For this reason a second pair of tubes had been installed into which they could plug their telephones to talk to each other. Wreaks was not connected up with these tubes, and when he wished to speak had to turn his head or wave his arm to attract their attention, after which they would plug in to listen to him. This arrangement of the speaking-tubes greatly increased the privacy of the rear cockpit and added to the estrangement of pilot and navigator.

Directly Shap saw the head in the cockpit in front of him turn round, he plugged his telephone into the tube to speak to him and corked up the other tube so Lily should not have the roar of the engine in her ears.

'Well, you took off marvellously, Jimmy,' he said. 'We're well away now. Aren't you going to take her up to 1000 feet?'

'No. Not till we get a bit lighter. I am leaving land at Bosworth coastguard station and setting a course five points north of east.'

'Right-o, I'll mark it.'

Lily Beanlands pulled out a stopper in the speaking-tube, and for a moment there was a roar in the pilot's ears interrupting his conversation and then the unpleasant scrape of metal as she plugged in.

'What a glorious take off, Jimmy! We are actually crossing the beach now. Do you realise? So it's good-bye to old England. Good-bye. Good-bye!'

'Yes. We're off at last,' answered Wreaks. The machine hit a bad bump as they left the cliff behind them and he corrected the lateral trim gently and firmly with a sideways pressure of the stick. Then he glanced at the compass again before he spoke.

'I expect to cross the Dutch coast at Alkmaar,' he said. 'We ought to do it in about an hour and twenty minutes.'

'Aren't you going higher up over the sea?' asked Lily.

'No. We may gain height gradually as we lose weight. At present we are too overloaded for it to be worth while to climb.' There was a silence.

'Oh, look! What a sweet boat! Like a toy,' said Lily. The men politely looked, bending their heads to look over the side directly down. Underneath them the men in the dinghy gazed up; their red upturned faces were bright spots against the greeny-blue sea. Beyond them a tug was setting out to sea, and the black mass of smoke pouring from the funnel preceded the little boat in a dirty ravelled fog over the blue waves, blown far ahead of her on her journey.

'Look at that for a west wind. Just what we want, a tail wind to help us on our way. We shouldn't have got off the ground so easily if it hadn't been for this wind,' said Wreaks to himself, but he did not remark on it to the others.

England was behind the aeronauts and already forgotten by them. They did not turn their heads for a last view of it. Before them a faint scum of dirtiness seemed to have gathered over the rim of the sea.

❀

The pupils at the flying club swooped one after another silently upon the porridge-coloured grass of the aerodrome, touched the wheels of the machines and bounced and bumped about on the ground for a moment before pushing the throttle wide and roaring off. . . .

Round and round the Moths circled, never still for long; never content to rest, until many hours later with folded wings they were packed close upon each other and left in the darkness of the hangars.

❀

In Asia the locusts whirled round and round in the late afternoon, pattering down on the dry reeds and startling other locusts into spasmodic flight.

The great monoplane roared through the air towards the east.

❀

When they reached Holland the land, even from a height of only 500 feet, was hazy and blurred with the milkiness of mist. Yet it was only half-past three and the sun was still quite high up.

There were people on the sands, children paddling and looking up at them, and a motor car ran along a road. But the whitish mist combined with the sunshine made everything seem unreal.

'Well, the most dangerous part of the trip is over,' said Shap, plugging in so that he could hear Wreaks reply.

'That's right. It's always nicer to feel that one can get down if one must. I believe this is just south of Alkmaar. Look and see if there isn't a big canal that turns in towards the town on the map. I guess that's it.'

Holland was an unreal world seen through smoked glass; a fogged plate with everything blurred and indistinct. Wreaks brought the machine still lower, but the ground did not gain reality as they approached it.

Black and white cattle threw up their tails and galloped on stiff-jointed legs scattering to the corners of the field, terrified by the giant above them. A pony drawing a hooded gig jogged along a narrow interminable road, and a woman in a sun-bonnet peered up at them from under the edge of the hood. She was holding the reins in her left hand. Tumbrils loaded with hay crossed the fields; from a haystack a man waved his prong and the pale sun cast a gleam on the steel points.

Shap suddenly became very busy map-reading and reporting their exact position to Wreaks. Lily Beanlands lay back in her seat with a smile of beatitude on her face. She was thinking: 'I am free now. It's funny to think that I am flying away from all of them—flying to fame. How silly Eileen's tennis seems now! And yet the fact that she was going to play in the Bournemouth tournament used to come before everything. Our whole lives were planned in the hopes that Eileen should get into the mixed doubles at Wimbledon, and she never did and never will.

We all had to think of Eileen all the time and, of course, none of them ever guessed what was in me. Even I never really quite believed that I was going to do something really great like this.

Well, now they'll know.

I'm happy at last after all those awful years when I was supposed to be a kitten: Alfred's kitten and Eileen's doormat. The boys were just as bad as Eileen really with Rugby and rock-climbing and winter sports.

'Good-bye, Lily. Sorry you always have to be left behind. It's hard luck. Good-bye, Lily. Don't get into mischief. Don't get too bored without us if we get snowed up for a couple of days in that beastly hut. So long, Lily, be good.'

It was silly of me to mind so much; I am much too sensitive, and I think I am rather romantic and proud with a streak of something wild. . . .

Since she had nothing better to do, and Wilmot was busy with his map, she thought about her own wildness for some time and then fell into a doze. For most of the time she was still aware that she was in her own aeroplane flying across Europe to break the long-distance record, but for a few minutes her mind slipped off to an odd, unpleasant memory. She believed that she was awake, so she could not be dreaming; at the same time she could not control her thoughts.

She was in a country-house with her stepchildren. . . . It was just before Guy Fawkes Day. A motor klaxon screamed wildly, and as a car pulled up, a boy and a girl of about twenty jumped out and charged up to the front door and pealed the bell. As the parlourmaid opened the door there was a noise of nailed boots clattering down the stairs at full speed, and as the elder children entered, a younger figure on the stairs charged down on them. There were yells of delighted laughter: young Leslie was wearing a comic mask with beetroot-pink cheeks and black whiskers. A moment later their father appeared on the landing of the stairs. His mask was appalling—an upturned Slavonic nose spreading bulbously on one side, a beetling forehead overhanging a pair of squint Mongolian eyes, while below sagged a pair of false indiarubber lips.

Lily followed him from her bedroom with a demure tread to welcome the children back. She had just powdered her face after wiping off the skinfood. Her complexion could hold its own with any girl's. A yell of delight greeted her, a yell which was followed by a momentary, appalling silence. Then Alfred pulled off his mask and began asking heartily about the journey. She kissed Eileen. John kissed her. Then as she followed Alfred into the dining-room she caught a whisper from the girl to her brother as they were hanging up their coats.

'That last phiz was the best of the three. D'you know I didn't recognise her. . . .'

❊

Just as they reached the outskirts of Hamburg they ran into rain.

'I'm going right up out of this mess,' said Wreaks. 'I don't like it at all.' He pressed his fingers gently back against the stick as though he were stroking a cat's throat and they rose, and as he did so he watched the needle of the A.S.I. travel back. It was travelling back fast, for they were very heavy and climbed with difficulty.

'We don't want to get all wet,' he thought, and pushed the knob of the throttle forward. 'I'll go up as fast as I can.'

The A.S.I. needle steadied itself and stopped at 90. The revolution counter showed 2250. The altimeter was trembling over the 1000-foot mark. Outside the cockpit nothing was visible; a white and clammy cloud enveloped them. 'This cursed weather must have been travelling down the Rhine,' he thought. 'The wind will have turned a bit southerly, we must allow for that.' He glanced casually at the turn indicator and inclinometer: the machine was level laterally.

Suddenly the cloud in which they were wrapped lightened. There was a whiteness ahead of them, sunshine behind them, a rainbow leapt against a cloud. They came out of the white fog into the blue sky, and as far as the eye could see, for hundreds of square miles stretched an immense snowfield, or ice-floe, of crystalline white cloud which seemed solid. Only rarely did it reveal a fluffy or woolly edge. This plain of snow was not continuous and smooth but like a Polar sea of ice, made up of tables and flattened ridges with fissures between them, but nowhere was there a hole through which one might catch a sight of the earth.

The scene was wildly pretty, like the heaven of the most heavenly Christmas pantomime, or a Victorian coloured stereoscopic view of Switzerland. But it was desert, desert as the moon. The pantomime chorus, dressed as angels with blue ribands and gold crowns: they weren't there. The sun blazed in a heaven of deep forget-me-not blue and threw the shadows of the heads of the travellers on to the cockpit dash in front of them. On the farthest horizon a range of majestic mountains rose up above the snowfield like Alpine peaks.

Lily Beanlands woke up. 'Oh, oh,' she whimpered. 'What a horrid brown study to fall into! What a horrible mask Alfred had put on, and poor Eileen. . . . It was almost like a dream . . . and it's odd because none of it ever happened, did it?'

She collected herself. Wilmot was bending towards her. She felt that to have fallen asleep would have been unpardonable. It would have shown no feeling for romance; it would have been a neglect of duty and a confession of age. Wilmot must not think that she had fallen asleep when she was only musing on the unhappy past.

She looked about her and suddenly realised that

they were flying above the clouds. Shap was plugging in to talk to her.

'Isn't it exquisite up here?'

'How high are we?' she asked, feeling that it was
a safe question.

'Four thousand. But though our speed drops a
little as we climb, we are much better off out of the
rain, and Wreaks told me he was going to fly at this
altitude until just before sunset, when I shall make
an exact determination of longitude. If the weather
is clear he intends to come down to confirm my
observations by spotting some town or river or railway and then he'll take us up again for the night.
And I can check our position at intervals by star
observations.'

They relapsed into silence.

There was so much time before them that they
both felt that they must be economical of their
enthusiasms and their talk, lest they should exhaust
all possibility of amusing and entertaining each
other. So Lily Beanlands spent several hours happily looking at the golden sunlight and the white
floor of the clouds, and then at the great powerful
wing and the instruments on the dash. Hours went
by, smiles and words were exchanged, and slowly
the sun sank behind them and the white mountains
ahead of them became tinged with pink reflections.
They had forgotten the passage of time; they were
lulled and hypnotised by the engine whose voice in
their ears had sunk from the first deafening roaring
to a faint bubbling drone, which at last was itself
but scarcely heard. Yet though unheard, it domin-

ated them, determining their mood. Everyone who has lived beside a waterfall will have had this experience. The roar of the torrent fades until only the tiny irregular noises in the flow are heard and these fade at last into a dream. But if the thoughts wander too far and impose a new mood on the dreamer the sound of the cataract returns suddenly in all its violence, jealous of new images which it drowns and washes from the mind.

Jimmy Wreaks turned in his seat. Shap was looking over the edge into vacancy, and the pilot could not attract his attention, so he closed the throttle and put the nose of the machine down. Directly afterwards he opened the throttle again and levelled out. By the time he had done this Shap was asking him what was wrong.

'Couldn't get you to notice me,' shouted Wreaks cheerfully. 'I want you to take a sextant reading, please.'

Shap felt unreasonably resentful at being woken from his day-dream and reminded of his duties by such drastic means, but he did not show he was annoyed.

'I'm afraid you will have to put the machine off her course so I can get the sun without twisting right round in my seat.'

Wreaks banked sharply and they swung round with a dipping wing. The sun was low down, and Shap busied himself for some time with his instruments. When he had made his readings, Jimmy banked the other way and swung back on to the original course.

'Between 54 and 55 latitude; and 18 longitude by the chronometer,' said Shap. 'I can't tell the latitude very exactly.'

'Where is it on the map?'

'About sixty miles north-west of Danzig, on the coast-line.'

'We can't be as far as that,' said Wreaks. 'Not unless we've had a most tremendous tail-wind all the way. Anyway I am going down to see.'

The setting sun was striking upon a far range of snow mountains, turning them to gold and scarlet, and the snowfield beneath paled to an ashy grey. Mrs. Beanlands and Commander Shap twisted themselves round in their seats to look at the red ball of the setting sun, and the slip-stream caught their raised heads, buffeting the raised tops of their helmets, insinuating itself in icy wedges under the protecting collars of fur, and reminding them, what they had almost forgotten, that they were in the air.

The tail fin and elevators were brilliantly clear-cut and black against the red sunset. Mrs. Beanlands noticed a frail wire leading to the rudder and sighed. Life was so wonderful! Everything was so marvellous! Wilmot's hand was resting on her elbow. This was first love! This was a wonderful comradeship!

The Baltic air drove like a wedge of ice into her great fur collar and stung her neck with cold. She looked at the black bars of cloud, at the red ball of the sun, at the black elevators, and moved her arm to lay her hand gently on Wilmot's wrist.

Wreaks closed the throttle and startled her with

the silence. The aeroplane was descending in a long glide, which seemed as though it might last for ever. The relief of silence was extraordinary. She looked at Wilmot and laughed, and he laughed back.

A few wisps of cloud caught the machine; it rocked violently, and down below, in front of them, appeared a level expanse of grey and empty sea, and far away, ahead of them, a line of white breakers and a bar of sand or shingle projecting far out. The sun had set. It was eight o'clock.

'It's where I said it was,' shouted Shap. 'That's the Putziger Bank. We're over the gulf of Danzig.'

'Good enough,' replied Wreaks. 'We've done wonderfully. I'm going up again now to get what's left of that tail-wind.'

The roar of the engine fell on them like the weight of a heavy pack taken up again at the end of a day's walk. For a while the sound cut cruelly into their nerves, then they forgot it and did not hear it. The bumps died away as they climbed again above the cloud.

The sky was full of stars; the earth below invisible except at long intervals when rare lights shone out also in that lower darkness. But the sky was transparent, even in its obscurity. It was very blue.

Wilmot Shap and Mrs. Beanlands began talking.

'What about some food?' she suggested. 'Will you have a sandwich or some of the hot coffee?'

It was delightful to move about a little in her seat groping for the parcel and the thermos. She snuggled down as low as she could, thinking: 'How cosy one can be. A woman like me can make any place that she is in seem like home.'

The hot coffee spilled on their lips and was blown out of the corners of their mouths.

Shap shouted jovially to the pilot: 'We're having supper. When are you going to have some?'

'No thanks. I'm all right. I'm going to have some coffee presently.'

While in the rear cockpit Wilmot and Lily crouched and gossiped and ate their sandwiches, throwing tight balls of crunched-up paper out into the darkness and whirlwind of the sky, Wreaks sat motionless scanning the illuminated dash in front of him with his one eye. Everything was going very well. Engine and oil and all the host of temperatures were quite healthy. 'I feel like a bloody research engineer in this outfit,' he said to himself. 'But God knows what it's all for. I can't put anything right if they go wrong. A chap might do a hurried forced landing and then discover it was only a broken thermometer that was wrong.'

After the sandwiches and coffee they ate a little punnet of strawberries in the rear cockpit and finally sent the little chip-basket flying over the side with the stalks and stems.

'Just a drop of brandy, Lily. And then I'm going to tuck you up for the night.'

'Oh, I couldn't possibly sleep. I couldn't dream of it. I'm far, far too excited,' answered Mrs. Beanlands.

'No, I shall take the first watch and then you can

take the second, if I can be spared,' said Shap firmly. 'I've got to make some observations of stars fairly soon.'

Wreaks shifted himself in his seat. He was feeling more tired than he expected and more bored. Behind him he could see a glimmer of light in the rear cockpit. For a little while his mind wandered and he thought of Burnaby. He remembered the engineer's shaking hand, shaking with whisky, and his big forehead. He was Burnaby's chum in the early days before he became a famous designer, and he had become Burnaby's test pilot afterwards. It had been bad for his nerves. It wasn't bad at first, but after 1925 he had got a hunch that old Burnaby was trying to kill him. 'He never was the same to me after I lost my eye. That's a funny thing to change a man. But he was never the same.' But old Burnaby was killed himself now. 'If one lives long enough one sees anything happen. Every possible combination comes to pass in time. Given infinite time seven monkeys typing at random will type the *Encyclopædia Britannica.*

'My hat, what a dotty joy-ride this is,' he reflected suddenly. 'If we come in for a strong headwind in Asia, hell only knows where we shall run out of petrol. But I guess I can last out as long as the tanks provided that we don't bump into any of those beastly mountains.'

The dashboard light went out in the rear cockpit. It certainly was like travelling *wagons-lits* when all was said and done, reflected Lily. She must speak to dear Mr. Wreaks before she went to sleep.

'Only, of course, I shan't be able to sleep for excitement.' She yawned, and the wind tore at the top of her weary widowed head.

'Wilmot.'

'Lily, darling.'

For a moment she felt suspicious and resentful. Wilmot mustn't go too far. Then she remembered suddenly that they were comrades on the great adventure.

'Lily, darling Lily. All my life seems to have been a preparation leading to this. The most exciting, the most miraculous night of my life, transcending love and war, and all rendered possible by you, you who make it all worth while. That's what I am feeling.' Shap gave a surprising warm, rich and gentle laugh at the end of this speech. 'If only I don't feel too terribly flat in the morning.'

Mrs. Beanlands took hold of his gloved hand and drew it to her. She was quite overcome by what Wilmot had said. For a moment or two they disputed which should kiss the other's gloved hand. Then Shap turned in his seat and, putting his hand on the leather-covered bosom of the lady, pressed his lips to hers. Gently he tucked her up.

'Good night, sweetheart. Good night.'

'Good night, dear comrade. I feel so safe with you.'

To make certain of making each other hear they had to whisper these soft nothings into the respective mouthpieces of their telephones, which involved turning their heads away from each other as they spoke.

For Jimmy the night grew stale and sickly, and he sat solidly for three hours, but after that he began to feel himself slip every little while. He blinked his eye fast and looked at the lighted dash and all the luminous dials in front of him. First he read them one after another in a slow circle anti-clockwise, then he read them in the reverse order. Hell, he was slipping again.

He moved, shook his shoulders, and reached for the thermos of black coffee. The bitterness roused him to wakefulness and he remembered the gleaming tramlines, the wet streets, the lorries under the bridge, near Camden Town, and the traffic moving forward in a confused mass. His car had skidded as he braked violently, and the Ford lorry turned sharply in on him with an absurdly late outflung driver's hand. Glass fell in ringing splinters on the pavement. A tram pulled up short to avoid him. A policeman appeared. He mustn't let the Bobby smell his breath or he would never get a job again, had been his thought as he remained seated in his car answering questions rather stiffly.

The bubble wavered, and he pressed the stick quickly, too quickly, to one side. Presently he would begin to remind himself of McCudden and tell himself stories of all the great pilots he had known.

Just behind him Shap sat perfectly awake and self-possessed. For some hours he let his mind play on all the possibilities of the flight. At their present rate there was quite a chance that they would succeed in reaching Hong-Kong. He saw himself in the Club with Lily, being given a lunch in her honour. It would be *her* flight, *her* aeroplane, *her* fame, and so her gratitude would embrace him. If they once made a success of it he knew that he would be sure of her. Rich, generous and, in spite of her propriety, amorous, she was bound to marry him if he played his cards properly.

Shap smiled wearily. There was no reason to be nasty about it. They would suit each other. A widow of forty has advantages and a girl of twenty has drawbacks. . . . But to get back to brass tacks.

A blast of air struck him on the cheek and he leant forward and screamed wildly: 'Wreaks! Hi, Wreaks! Wake up!' The machine rocked violently and the wind in his face vanished.

'I say, old man, hadn't you better take her up a bit higher. Just in case you know. . . .'

'That's all right. That's my look-out. I let her skid a bit just now, but the bubble's rather hard to see in this light.'

Shap threw himself into conversation. At all events the pilot had to be kept awake. But Jimmy Wreaks would not answer. Shap's voice ringing in his ears exasperated him. It was queer how he had put on rudder unconsciously. He could only think that he must have dozed a little and pushed out one leg and drawn the other in without thinking what he was doing. He shook himself and looked about him. There was a lighter patch of sky in the east, but it couldn't be the dawn. 'I guess it's the moon. That will wake me up a bit when it rises. The sky is light enough in all conscience.'

He looked at the instruments in turn, then put his hand in his pocket and pulled out a brandy flask and gulped a big mouthful. The brandy burned him, it warmed him, he felt its glowing fingers run all through him caressing his numb body. It was fine. But that infernal fellow was still jabbering in his ear.

'How are you feeling, old chap? Will you give the air-speed reading?'

Wreaks groaned with annoyance and pulled out the connection of his telephone. The vast roar of the engine immediately replaced the insistent voice of the navigator.

'That's got rid of him for a bit,' he thought. Shap remained in ignorance of what had happened and went on talking and asking questions to which he got no reply. In a little while he was vowing vengeance secretly, but the explanation of the pilot's silence did not occur to him. The moon rose, and an hour later a grey crack was opening on the horizon. Half an hour later the dawn was breaking in the first pinks and pearl grey with a touch of gold. The stars had grown pale and disappeared. Below the earth was hidden, and a pearly white sheet stretched as far as the eye could see. They appeared to be flying over a vast waveless sheet of water.

'I make out that we are somewhere in the heart of Russia,' Shap said to himself. 'But can we have drifted north to Lake Ladoga? We must have done, and I can't get any answer out of that lunatic.'

Jimmy felt singularly happy and at peace with

all the world. He wasn't tired or sleepy any longer and looked about him cheerily. At last the sun's rim appeared over the horizon and blinded him, and he hastily pulled out the cork with which he had plugged up the end of his telephone and connected it up so that he could hear what Shap had to say, and shouted:

'Good morning, Commander. Will you please note the time by the chronometer and give me our approximate longitude?'

'What's been the matter with you, eh? I'm glad you've found your voice again,' grumbled Shap angrily.

Jimmy burst into uncontrolled guffaws. 'I say, I am sorry. I ought to have warned you. I disconnected my headphones in order to listen to the engine. I thought I heard something funny about it, but it was quite all right.'

'Oh, that's all right, Wreaks. No harm done. Why, we must be in longitude thirty-six. We've done marvellously.'

The two men were on good terms again. Shap thought: 'If only I could have a wash and a cigarette, I should feel all right for another twenty-four hours.' A mouthful of neat whisky cheered him.

Looking down he saw that what he had taken for water was a ground mist which vanished as he watched. It was lucky he had not spoken about it and given himself away.

Half an hour later Lily Beanlands woke up and looked about her. The sun falling directly into her eyes had woken her. She blinked. For a minute everything was red and black while her dream of a vast cascade of water, of Niagara Falls, in which Alfred, her husband, was being washed away, haunted her. She moved, and seeing Wilmot sitting beside her, she smiled at him. The roar of Niagara was the roaring of the engine. When she looked over the side of the cockpit, Russia seemed to her like a newly varnished toy which had only just been made. Below her she saw a rolling hill, a scattered forest of birch trees with open glades, which ran down to a wide uncultivated heath, where the birches were few and a great peat bog opened before her with regular squares and oblongs of cut peat with water lying in each and the turves standing beside them in cubical brown stacks. There was a light railway running through the forest to carry them away.

A screen of firs and birches cut off the heath, and they crossed a narrow road with two lodges by a park wall. Beyond, in the park, was a ruined house, and farther on a hamlet with a green-roofed church with a blue cupola. There were goats grazing round the church. One of them was perched on the broken wall of brick which ran round the church. Then came more birch trees and waste land and peat cutting, and the links of a river winding among fields. And then more birch trees and more rivers and stacks of peat.

Wreaks was waving his arm and pointing: on the horizon to the south-east there was something gold and white glittering in the sunlight. The aeroplane banked suddenly in a steep turn towards it and she plugged in.

'Moscow.'

'Moscow! Are we going to fly over Moscow?' Over the Kremlin, where those dreadful Commissars plot to do away with rich people.

'They won't shoot at us, will they?' she asked anxiously. Wreaks laughed, a deep hearty laugh, and she felt reassured. Her fears of Bolshevism, and of Russia, subsided as the spectacle of Moscow unfolded itself.

From a distance the city seemed a cluster of white points, each tipped with gold, but as they drew closer the whole city, the expanse of houses and gardens, became dominated by an immense white building crowned with an enormous golden dome. The huge compact cathedral was the heart of Moscow: it seemed almost the whole of it, and only as they came closer could she make out in detail the Kremlin: a vast palace bordering the river beside the bridge, and surrounded by a jumble of domes and cupolas, and towers of lesser buildings with courtyards between them. She could see a piece of the wall running round it and a square on the other side, and then the town spreading out dingily into a great expanse beyond.

They were almost too high to notice the people in the streets, or to see if they stopped to look up at them. Beyond Moscow there were railway lines and huge fields of greeny yellow rye, and lines of pollard willows, a lake by a factory and a windmill on a piece of rising ground.

They had breakfast. The wonderful, marvellous experience of seeing Moscow from the air had delayed it, and they drank the hot coffee and ate the ham sandwiches and talked for some time enthusiastically about Moscow and about their flight.

When their powers of conversation were exhausted, Lily Beanlands got out her diary and her fountain pen and set to work.

'*The greatest adventure of my life,*' she headed it, and spent two happy hours in composition.

'How wonderful it will seem of me to have written it in the air actually before the end of our adventure, not yet knowing whether we shall fail or triumph,' she thought.

'*I begin to believe that we shall break the record,*' she wrote. '*That record which has been the object of our thoughts for months.*' The business about the record was, she remembered, rather a complicated one. She must ask Wilmot about it later. She always forgot.

Jimmy turned and waved his hand. Wilmot tapped her elbow.

The Volga!

'Oh, Wilmot! The Volga. How wonderful. How marvellous. How romantic. The Volga! Just think, the Volga!'

Wreaks smiled savagely as these raptures reached him.

'What the hell does the woman think happens if you make a bee-line across Europe?' he said to himself. 'You must get somewhere if you burn all this petrol.'

The river itself was, when they looked at it, extremely fine. It was very wide, and they could see a steamer going up and another coming down. And there were three islands in a row.

'South of Kazan,' announced Shap. 'We've come a good way south of our route you know. In three or four hours we ought to get to the Urals.'

Mrs. Beanlands went back to her log and began describing the Volga.

'*I almost thought of asking Jimmy to stop the engine and glide down in the hope that we should hear a snatch of the boat-song wafted up to us. But such nonsense must not be allowed to come between us and our great objective.*'

There was no longer anything they could do. It had become boring looking at Russia. Lily and Wilmot connected up their telephones and talked for a couple of hours brightly about the French coast, discussing each little town between Marseilles and Mentone all the way along the Riviera, each with its hotels and casinos, when they had each been there, what local inhabitants they had met, the prices they had paid, the weather they had enjoyed and the awful occasions when they had been ill abroad and had to call in a French doctor.

They no longer noticed how time went and had forgotten where they were.

'We're in sight of the Urals. We crossed a railway about five minutes ago. I want you to spot our exact position.'

Shap became busy. 'We've not done quite so well,' he announced.

'Asia!' cried Lily. 'We're crossing into Asia!' To their surprise the Urals looked quite a fine range of mountains. A big peak stood up to the south, and they bumped a bit. But after a quarter of an hour Asia became very much like Europe, and after a technical conversation Shap returned to discuss the Éden Roc hotel at Antibes. Talking of hotels made them hungry, and they munched chocolate and malted milk tablets. Wreaks joined in and ate chocolate and malted milk himself. Then he drank a little brandy. He was beginning to ache in different places and suffer from pins and needles.

They flew over a lake and identified it, and slowly the hours dragged by. The sun sank low; at four-thirty, Greenwich time, it set.

'We can't be far from Akmolinsk,' said Shap.

'There are two serious dangers now,' announced Wreaks suddenly in ringing tones. 'The first is that a northerly wind should have been drifting us down to Kizyl Rai and that we should hit it. That isn't very likely. The other is that I should run into the Tarbagata or the Narym Mountains before dawn. Will you please check for wind drift by dropping a flare?

It was obvious even to Lily that Wreaks was seriously worried because they had not identified their position before darkness fell.

'The only thing which may save us is the moon. Only I don't know when it rises.'

As Wreaks betrayed anxiety, Shap became propitiatory and deferential and put forward consoling suggestions with the utmost tact. But Jimmy was not to be made easy in his mind, and kept Shap busy making observations again and again, and made him read out his calculations to him.

He was torn between the desire to push on as fast as possible (in which lay their only chance of reaching Hong-Kong) and a terror of arriving while it was still dark in the vicinity of mountains 14,000 feet or more high. As time went on it became clear that he was becoming definitely nervous. The earth was invisible, not a light showed on it, but after five hours the sky grew paler ahead of them. Half an hour later the moon rose, revealing the peaks of a great mountain range.

'Those must be the Narym Mountains. The Altai,' said Shap.

'Well, it has come out just in time. I shan't bump into them now.'

The moon rose higher and the mountains showed black and surprisingly clear. Suddenly another range appeared closer to them on their right. 'That's splendid!' shouted Jimmy. 'Just what we ought to find.'

A bump struck them, and the machine rocked violently. Another bump. Flying became a new and difficult art, and Wreaks had to put his head inside the cockpit and watch the illuminated dash and winking little green and red lights of the turn indicator.

The mountains were becoming near and awe-inspiring, and Wreaks banked the machine and swung off on a north-easterly compass course.

'Here's the lake, Jimmy,' said Shap, delighted with the good news.

The soft moonlight gleamed over an unmistakable stretch of water. Jimmy looked out at the great mountain ranges towards which he was flying, shutting him in ahead and on his right. They were not black in the moonlight but all sorts of subdued colours, purple, violet, brown and dusky blue with dull silvery ribs of glacier shining softly in the yellow moonlight, and while the machine rocked, fighting the wind which blew off them, he licked his lips and stared.

'That's what I came for,' he whispered to himself. 'My God, I'm not too old yet. This is the lake and we keep straight over it until we spot the Irtysh. Damn it all, I wish Donald was here, or somebody that understood. It would have just sent him crazy.'

Donald had been an observer of Jimmy's. He had been dead thirteen years.

'If there were any clouds now, or fog, we should be dead men.'

The mountains drew together and overhung them. The lake narrowed and the silvery bar of the river stretched away between the shadows of the mountains.

Jimmy grunted an assent as Shap called out: 'The Irtysh!' but his heart sang: 'The Irtysh. I've found the Black Irtysh in the dark, and here comes the dawn in a glory of fire over the snows of the Altai. At last I'm living again. It's damn fine. It's grand.'

But instead of such words he answered: 'Give me the compass course for the river. I'll fly by compass for a bit, and then come back to it so you can estimate our drift.'

The machine was needing a great deal of careful flying. The great mountain peaks drew close and their progress was slow.

'It's a head-wind!' The mountains were changing colour. On the left they were shadows of blue, hanging in screens, range behind range, like the wings and scenery running off the stage. But on the right they had been touched by the first rays of the sun and were solid, yellow, golden, green and veined with black. The sun blazed up over Eastern Turkestan, the wind backed to the north, and for a time they made more progress.

Two hours after dawn, as they passed over the Dzungarian uplands, just to the north of Bogda-ola, which rose to a height of 22,000 feet in a sheer cliff, they ran into a head-wind. It was bumpy and violent, and for a time Wreaks had his hands full. But far worse than the bumps was the fact that the ground speed fell off noticeably.

An hour later, when they had left Bogda-ola behind them, they began to climb steadily, and Wreaks swung the machine due south. 'Here we go over the pass,' explained Shap; but Lily didn't like the pass, though, of course, the mountains were simply titanic. But the pass was too bumpy altogether until she saw the earth drop away into a deep valley. Jimmy skirted the valley and began to take the machine down. They passed over a mud town. 'There is Hami, and ahead of us we should see the Pe-shan.' The head-wind was awful.

'I'll go as low as I can and see if I can get along a bit faster,' said Jimmy. For the next hour they flew very low down, rocking and bumping violently in the wind.

The land was a broken country of desert. Rocks of all shapes and sizes, from pebbles to haystacks, were scattered thickly over a flattish plain, which became broken up into a hilly region as they approached the foothills of a mountain range, behind which, in the south, Wreaks could catch sight of the snow-capped range of the Nan-shan.

Suddenly a few drops of oil appeared on the little windscreen in front of him, and before his mind could grasp what was happening a stream of oil was being sprayed back from under the engine cowling over his face and helmet. He ducked his head instinctively, but he could not avoid the shower of oil which covered his goggles and blinded him. Instinctively he shut the throttle and switched off the engine, and then, driven desperate by the oil, banked the machine and held its nose up with top rudder, sideslipping wildly into wind, and pushing his goggles off as he did so, to see with his one eye. The rocks rushed at them from the tilted wing. Rocks, rocks, rocks. Nothing but rocks, and a stretch where large pebbles lay thickly in a blue and white bed at the bottom of a dry water-course, overhung by low bluffs of earth.

Wreaks no sooner saw this spot than he put the nose of the machine down and turned her quickly

on the glide, and then pulling the nose sharply up, sideslipped right down on to the rocky edge of the bluff. The rocks rushed up into Lily Beanlands' face, the rush of wind tore her face as they dropped. As they almost touched the cliff's edge, Wreaks checked the slip sharply and glided down on to the bed of the stream. The passengers behind him lurched each way as he swish-tailed violently, slowing the machine until he knew that it must crash. At the last moment Wreaks put the stick back a bit more—a bit more, and deliberately stalled four feet above the earth. Bounce! Crash! They had hit one of the bigger boulders ahead, and the tail of the machine rose in the air, the left side of the undercarriage collapsed, the wing-tip caught in the stones and splintered and tore. All was suddenly still, in a state of perfect repose. Everything had been quiet; it seemed for a very long while, ever since the engine had been switched off.

In the quietness they could hear Shap swearing. He had tried to jump clear and had been jerked back by his headphones. Wreaks was in pain. His left foot was trapped and twisted. He could not extricate it from between the rudder bar, which had been pushed up, and a strut of the undercarriage which had come up through the fuselage. Lily Beanlands was very collected.

'We ought to get out quickly in case the machine should catch fire.' After saying this she detached her telephone connection and climbed out unaided, on the right side of the machine, from which she had to jump some way down to the ground.

Shap had already jumped out on the left. Wreaks remained immovable, twisting his crushed foot laboriously. At last he got it free, unstrapped his belt, disconnected his telephone, and pulled himself up out of the cockpit with his hands. Then he slid gently over the side of the fuselage.

The three of them stood in front of the machine and looked at it.

'Oil-pipe bust,' said Wreaks.

The nose of the aeroplane was lying on the ground, the left-hand side of the undercarriage had telescoped up, and the left wing was bent back and shattered at the tip. Petrol was dripping from a buckled tank in the left wing, and all the front of the machine glistened green-bronze with oil. It did not occur to any of the three to begin to do anything. Commander Shap and Mrs. Beanlands stood huddled together, surveying the wreckage. Jimmy Wreaks sat down on the ground, and began to untie the laces of the boot on his crushed foot. At intervals Shap walked round the wreck and came away from it again.

Then he climbed up the steep bluff or cliff of earth which was the bank of the dry river in which they had come down. When he reached the top he called to Mrs. Beanlands.

'Come up, will you, Lily? You can see a lot of the country here. Will you bring my field-glasses with you?'

Mrs. Beanlands set off; she climbed and slipped on the friable, shaly, dry clay, and when she was three-quarters of the way up the almost vertical bank, she got stuck and called to Wilmot Shap to help her. Jimmy looked up at the shaky figure, making uncertain movements, and grinned pityingly at her embarrassment.

After Shap had hauled her up, they did not come back for some time, and Jimmy dozed away the worst of the sickening pain.

Shap was speaking. 'My word, it was hot up there moving about.' Wreaks looked at the perspiring faces and listened.

'It's real desert. There's hardly any vegetation except a prickly sort of whin and a few patches of stonecrop. Otherwise it's all stones and rocks. . . . We didn't see any other possible landing-place. We were lucky to get down here. And now we'll have lunch and consider plans afterwards, when we're all more recovered.'

They ate three rather stale sandwiches, each with varying degrees of enjoyment, and then munched some chocolate, after which Jimmy dozed off again like a drugged man. Mrs. Beanlands took the rest of the food and put it away in the cockpit, and Shap climbed once more up the bluff with a map in his hand and sat in the shade of a big rock, smoking his pipe. Wreaks, who was a cigarette smoker, had come without any. Shap did not offer him his pipe tobacco.

Long shadows fell from every stone; dusk gathered in the distances; the wind dropped and a chill fell on the wrecked voyagers. Wreaks sat cross-legged in pain, fingering the swollen instep and ankle, while Shap moved to and fro, hunting through the 'plane hoping to find something useful. He brought out the food. There was very little left: a parcel or two of sandwiches, an untouched thermos of black coffee and another of hot milk, half a pound of nut-milk chocolate, a tube of Horlick's tablets.

Mrs. Beanlands, who had slipped off, came back, having discovered a tiny runnel of water on the opposite side of the river-bed. She went back to it with an empty thermos and filled it with water.

'I'm going to make some malted milk,' she announced. 'What can I burn, Mr. Wreaks?'

'Tear off a bit of that wing fabric,' he suggested. 'But bring it right away from the 'plane or we shall have the whole thing in a blaze.'

The darkness seemed to fall faster for the little flame. Lily Beanlands had to heat the water a cupful at a time, in the metal tops of the thermos flasks. She held them in a pair of pliers she took out of the tool locker.

'Here you are, Jimmy, I am so sorry about your poor foot. But isn't it wonderful? To be alive, I mean.'

Wreaks was grateful for the hot malted milk and felt that it had done him good, but he was too exhausted to speak and in too much pain. Moreover, he had not even yet finished cursing himself for letting the accident catch him when he was flying so low. 'If I had had 500 feet in hand I could have put her down somewhere safely and have mended the oil-pipe. But now we are done.

Finish. And to be stranded with such a pair of ghastly love-birds. Poor old girl, I suppose it's not her fault, but I wish the family had kept her under restraint.'

He sat rubbing the strained ligaments and cursing himself silently until sleep swiftly came, and his head dropping on to his arms, he collapsed, fast asleep, pillowed on some scattered stones.

❀

He was woken by Shap shaking him by the arm.

'Hey, what's that?' he said fiercely, quarrelsome in his sleep and then blinking his one eye open upon the world. The sun was shining brilliantly, already high up in a cloudless blue sky.

'She wouldn't let me wake you before, but it's time we were moving, old boy. You and I have got to have a council of war.'

Jimmy spat. Then he stood up, and a stab of pain reminded him of his ankle. A small fire was smoking a few yards from the wrecked aeroplane, and the smoke rose in a thin column straight up in the air.

'No wind,' Wreaks noted automatically. But what did the wind matter? That 'plane would never fly again.

'Look here, Wreaks,' said Shap in a low voice. 'I'm responsible for Mrs. Beanlands' safety. We've got to find some natives. We've got to leave you here until we can send for you, because of your foot.'

'That's all right,' said Jimmy, putting his hand over his mouth and yawning.

'I want to start at once. You realise that I must take what's left of the food, don't you? Also one of the compasses, although it's so heavy.'

'Come and have a cup of malted milk, Jimmy,' called Mrs. Beanlands, climbing out from the cockpit of the aeroplane. 'I wouldn't let Wilmot wake you before. Aren't you grateful? You were in such a sound sleep. You were really, and you deserved it. The more I have been thinking over our descent, the more I am convinced that we all owe our lives to you.'

Wreaks took the thermos top in his handkerchief and lifted it to his lips.

'Have you had your breakfast, Mrs. Beanlands?' he asked, feeling strangely solicitous for this woman's welfare. 'I'm afraid I've been precious little use.'

'We've had ours. There are two sandwiches for your breakfast as well. We've each had two sandwiches. Wilmot has worked out that we must be really quite close to China.' She laughed. 'So we are going to go off, leaving you, and find some Chinese.'

Wreaks laughed, and took the two sandwiches from her and wrapped them up in his handkerchief.

'Wilmot is desperately anxious to set off at once. Of course, we can't tell how far we may have to walk to get help.'

Wreaks sat down and sipped the malted milk

meditatively. It was delicious. He was surprised that Mrs. Beanlands should turn out so well in an emergency.

'Are you ready to start, Lily?' called Shap. 'We want to get off before the heat of the day.'

'I'm leaving you one of the empty thermos flasks; it will do to carry water in if you can get as far as the stream with your poor foot,' said Lily.

Wreaks struggled to his feet and hopped up to her.

'I should like to say I think you are a very plucky woman. You've been very kind. . . . It has been a great pleasure. . . . I wish I had put up a better show.' They took each other's hands rather emotionally.

'Well, till to-morrow. I hope we shall be able to send for you to-night—but if not, then to-morrow.'

'Good-bye.'

'Good-bye.'

'Good luck. Don't overdo the first day's march if you can't find any natives.'

'We shall be all right, old chap.'

'Good-bye.'

They crossed the bed of the river and began to climb the opposite bank, picking their way carefully and moving slowly and laboriously. At the top they turned to wave. They were black figures standing against the sun. Jimmy pulled himself up to attention and gave a military salute. Then they were gone.

'Now I settle down and make myself cosy,' he said to himself. He finished the last drop of the malted milk and, taking the sandwiches out of his

pocket, hopped with them in his hand to the aeroplane.

'She wasn't a bad woman. I always knew she had
guts, only she was a damned fool to want to come
on this trip.'

Shap had taken the map for this section with him,
and Jimmy regretted he had not discussed their
position with him before he left. Perhaps it was
marked in the log. His own belief was that they
were about fifty or a hundred miles north of a line
connecting An-hsi-chow and Su-chow. His ankle
unfortunately prevented him from climbing up on
the bluff and viewing the country. All he could see
was the bed of the dry water-course in which the
'plane lay, and the cliff, or wall of earth, which
bounded it on the other side. He was hungry and
the sun was hot. 'When shall I eat the first sandwich?' he asked himself, looking at the little parcel
in his hand.

'To-night, at nine o'clock, I will eat it, and to-
morrow night I will eat the second.' But thinking
of time, as a hungry man must, reminded him that
he should wind the chronometer in case it should
run down. His wrist watch had stopped; he had
forgotten it the previous night. He hopped along
the side of the fuselage to the rear cockpit, balan-
cing himself by gripping the edge. Then laying his
precious sandwiches on the fuselage, he drew himself up with difficulty and seated himself in Shap's
seat. First he put away the sandwiches in a pigeon-
hole in the dash, then he wound the chronometer,
which was ticking. It read 12.48, and for a moment

he was puzzled, but he soon realised that it was A.M. That was by English summer-time; by local (perhaps Indian) time it must have been about seven o'clock in the morning.

He glanced at the maps which were left and picked up Shap's sextant. On Mrs. Beanlands' seat there were lying her heavy fur coat, her flying helmet and goggles, and her electrically heated flying-suit. In the pocket at the back of Shap's seat was a notebook with what she had written of the LOG OF THE WAYZGOOSE, and stuck among its pages two unposted addressed letters which she must have written on the journey. There was a small parcel of some of her clothes.

Jimmy decided to make an inventory of useful objects sometime later in the day. But, at the moment, what did it matter what he did or did not do? He was alone, absolutely alone, and had to wait fourteen hours before he ate a sandwich. Until then he could pass the time as he liked.

Scruples held him back from reading Mrs. Bean-lands' diary of the flight, though he was certain that it would amuse him. He laid it unopened in the pigeon-hole on top of the sandwiches, telling himself that he must remember to take it and her letters with him when the Chinese, or Mongolians, or Tibetans, arrived to fetch him, if they ever did. It might easily take Shap three days before he reached a village, or fell in with a shepherd. The shepherd would take him and Mrs. Beanlands to the headquarters of the tribe; the headman might take them on to the nearest Chinese official, so that an expedition to rescue him would probably not set out till the fourth or fifth day. It might take as much as two days to reach him, even for mounted men. Thus, his rescue might not take place for a week, but if nine days went by he would know that there was no hope.

'On the other hand, it may be to-morrow,' he said aloud, and laughed.

'There is one great consolation: thank God, I haven't got a broken leg, or she would have stayed here to nurse me. Hoo! Hoo! Think of that! Think of being left with a woman without a bite of food for a week or a fortnight! Fancy offering to let her eat me, or else making up my mind to eat her! One couldn't toss up for a thing like that with a woman.'

Such thoughts put Jimmy in a good humour and made him forget his hunger for a little while. But he grew thirsty.

'I'll go and look at the spring or whatever it is, where she found water.'

He climbed out, and after unscrewing one of the undercarriage struts to serve as a staff to support himself, he hobbled across the bed of the watercourse, or *wady*, as he called it, from his experience of Arabia. The ground was thickly strewn with round pebbles and cobble-stones, interspersed with a few larger boulders. The bed of the *wady* was perhaps a hundred yards across. The aeroplane had crashed on the left-hand northern side of it, which Wreaks had chosen at the last moment as the boulders were fewer there. On the far side was a little trickle of water running among the stones, expanded here and there in its course into shallow stagnant puddles, marked by a clump of reeds or coarse grass. On the bed of the *wady* itself there was no vegetation growing among the white and blue polished pebbles. Wreaks scooped up water to wash his hands and face, then he filled the empty thermos with water and drank his fill, and then made a little pit in the bed of the trickle of water and held his injured foot in it.

The water was pleasant and refreshing, though not very cold. It tasted of iron. 'It's handy,' he said. 'But what a place to crash!'

When he turned and saw the machine lying in a river-bed among so many broken boulders and big rocks he marvelled how he had got down without worse damage.

There were no traces of life at the pool; no footprints of beasts or birds. 'There must be other water not far off that they prefer,' he argued. 'I shall have to shoot something for supper. I've got my pistol.'

He had left it in the front cockpit of the aeroplane and a sudden fear that Shap had taken it assailed him, and he began to hobble back after he had filled up the thermos flask again.

How lonely the dry river-bed with its loosely cobbled floor and the white wings lying broken under the sunshine of Mongolia! How lonely! How silent to ears jaded by the roar of engines never ceasing day or night! How silent! Solitude, loneliness, emptiness, silence—Wreaks had experienced these often enough when planing down with a

shut throttle from a height of 20,000 feet above
the earth, through a desert of cloud forms or
phantom Polar sea. At such times he would hear
nothing but the *whick, whick, whick* of the slowly
spinning airscrew and would see no living thing in
the desert about him unless, perchance, it were the
moving phantom of himself: his shadow.

But he was not at the mercy of the desert of the
sky. He was free, happy as a living bird, full of
mastery. With a movement of his thumb he could
make the empty spaces echo and in ten minutes
he could descend gently among the 'planes which
circled about the grassy aerodrome. If he were
pressed for time he could put the machine in a spin
and come down as fast as the angels falling out of
heaven, watching the earth appear through the
clouds and open out to him while it revolved like a
roulette wheel slowly coming to rest. In a minute
he could be listening to empty-headed laughter and
a jazz record on the gramophone.

But in this desert of the earth he moped feebly,
seeking shade by lying under the monoplane's
broken wing and rousing himself only to look at the
fractured steel of the undercarriage.

Five pebbles were balanced on the dead-white
scarred back of a hand. The wrist flicked and four
were caught in the palm. But the game of knucklebones is played the other way: thrown up from
the palm and balanced on the back of the hand.
Three stayed and two rolled off. Two stayed and
three fell. Four stayed and one fell. One remained,
balanced alone, and four were scattered. . . . But

at all events they clinked together making a sound to break the monotony of hunger.

If he could not take a siesta, he could lie with his eye tightly shut; if he could not forget food, he could tighten his belt. He could make a target of a pebble balanced on a rock and sit in the shade and throw others to knock it off.

For the last hour before sunset he sat and massaged his foot, resolving to spend the whole of the next morning in the same dismal occupation, since as soon as the inflammation went down he would be able to move about and find something to eat. He could not climb the bluff until his foot was better, and the thought came to him that there might be herds of sheep, or, who knows, yaks, grazing within sight on that stony land, or a line of Bactrian camels crossing the desert laden with rhubarb, within a mile of where he lay starving. At last the sun began to set and he climbed up into the cockpit where he had laid his sandwiches. It was only two minutes to three by the chronometer. The sun set at twenty past nine in England, and he decided that he would go by local time for his meals. Otherwise he would have to keep himself awake at night and eat in the dark.

He took out one sandwich and ate it very slowly, crumb by crumb, washing it down with a pint or so of water. The other sandwich he put away, though he was ravenously hungry after his meal, and as he drew on his airman's leather suit and the fleece-lined thigh boots, the fur gauntlets and the fur-lined hat, it seemed to him that he never would be able to go to sleep. But he was still weary after his flight and exhaustion gained the victory over hunger. After half an hour he was peacefully asleep, his last thought being a hope that he would be awakened by the crunch of footsteps on the loose stones.

The sun was hot upon him; he was drenched in sweat and his head ached. It was late, and he had been sleeping for hours in his thick fur-lined leather suit. The stones near him were hot to the touch when he sat up. He felt ill and faint with hunger, and staggering on to his feet hobbled painfully to the 'plane, pulled the sandwich out of its hiding-place and looked at it.

'I daresay a rescue party will be here by lunch-time with gallons of hot bovril,' he said to himself and took a bite. Angrily and reluctantly he ate the two slices of desiccated bread and the withered slice of tongue that curled black and greasy between their roughness. A crumb fell, and when he had finished he went down on hands and knees to pick over the stones until it was retrieved.

That day was terrible. His hunger increased. He sipped water continually but without quenching his thirst, and his heaviness and headache were so great that he thought a sunstroke could be the only cause. But worse than all physical pains was the torture of anticipation. At every moment he was looking up quickly, thinking to see mounted figures appear on the opposite bank of the river and wave to him. He would wave back and they would descend, leaning back on their horses' haunches at a spot about half a mile away, where the slope was not so steep. He looked towards it with his hawk's eye, and the stones wavered in a mist of heat under the sun.

His tongue was furry and his throat was sore. He struggled with difficulty to the runnel of water, and, never having been ill before in his life, became convinced that he was dying.

'I do believe that I am going to croak. I do honestly,' he said aloud in a strange voice that evening, as he sat massaging the purple flesh of his bruised ankle and instep, and he determined to resort to his last hope in the most desperate of emergencies: his brandy flask, which he had hidden so that he should be out of the way of temptation.

For a moment or two he thought that he would not be able to pull himself up by the struts into the cockpit, for his head spun and his strength seemed to have gone. But he pulled and struggled, and his heavy body seemed suddenly to be released by something that had been holding it down.

He took a gulp of brandy while he sat in the cockpit, then, feeling restored, climbed out. His head still ached, and his stomach whined for food, but his weakness was gone. Before drinking again he pulled on his airman's clothes and went to lie down in the bed he had made of Mrs. Beanlands' fur coat and the seats of the cushions, under the broken wing. As he crawled into this kennel the effort made him sweat violently and his head felt as though it were splitting. Another pull at the brandy flask stopped him from actually crying out with the pain. The brandy ran like fire down his arms; it glowed deliciously in his stomach and crept in a fiery embrace round to the small of his back, but it was the taste of it on his tongue which delighted him beyond everything. It was so delicious a flavour that he reflected bitterly on the cruel fate which allowed him to have such an agonising pain in his head to distract him while he was drinking it. He sipped again, and then drank a great gulp. It was nectar; the smell of it tickled his nostrils; the volatile spirit was inhaled into his lungs. He drank another mouthful and his headache was gone. He lay disembodied, almost swooning in bliss, savouring the brandy, not disturbed by the softly swaying earth that rolled beneath him and slipped away from him ever so gently.

'Earth-pockets. There are earth-pockets,' he said, delighted at the new thought. 'But I don't care. I'm so damned stable. It's the hot days and the cold nights: contractions, expansions. . . .'

Lifting the flask to his lips, he drained it of the last drop. The contractions and expansions swayed him, and then suddenly the earth beneath him began to move round and round like a top, and he felt himself moving with it.

'A spin. I'm spinning. Opposite rudder. I haven't been drunk like this since I was a boy, and on less than half a bottle of brandy! I didn't know it was possible. Spin again. I won't! I won't!'

As his will hardened he felt himself oscillate like the needle of a compass; then he was lying perfectly still in bed. His will relaxed and he felt himself begin to turn again, but before he had done two turns he was asleep.

The light was fresh and innocent, and Wreaks looked out upon a jumbled floor of clean cobblestones and the far bank of the dry river throwing its shadow over him.

'It's early yet,' he said to himself. 'But I have slept well and am recovered.' The pangs of hunger had diminished, and his head was clear. Best of all, however, was that his ankle was much less swollen; indeed, it seemed to be quite well until he rose up and put his weight on it.

No sooner had he stood up than he lay down again, for there was nothing he could do during the day, except play knucklebones and fetch himself water from the runnel, and he was not anxious to start the day early. But before he composed himself to sleep again he pulled off his airman's clothing and his fur helmet. The air was warm already, and it would bring on another headache if he lay sweating wrapped up in furs. Sleep did not come easily, and he lay with his thoughts, not coloured either by bitterness or by affection, playing round the figure of his wife in England.

She had married him on his first leave after he had got his wings, during the war, in December 1916, and he thought with regret of the R.F.C. uniform. How fond he had been of his little forage cap with the tiny line of red piping! But he would not let his mind stray to the R.F.C. He would think of his wife.

She was never the same to him after he was so

badly burnt; perhaps it would be truer to say that he was never the same to her. With most women it would not have made any difference: most women would have been proud of the cross they gave him when he was thought to be dying—but she never seemed proud of him, only numbed with horror. His temper was terrible for a time, he knew that, but it was the scars that upset her most. That was odd.

Directly he was able to pass a medical board he asked to be allowed to go out to France again, but he was sent as an instructor to Scotland instead. Daphne did not go with him. After his medical board she had said, astonished: 'Surely you're not going to fly again, Jimmy.' Nothing she had said or done, wounded him as much as that. She couldn't understand why he did.

Well, he had flown again; and then, of course, he had had that nasty crash in 1924 when he lost his eye. It was while he was at home convalescent that he found out that Daphne was having a love-affair with a schoolmaster. She begged him not to divorce her.

'I swear to be faithful to you, Jimmy. I swear to be a good wife.' Now if he didn't turn up; if he were to starve to death she would presume his death and marry the fellow. Daphne herself would never go up in a 'plane, and was frightened for her own safety when he flew low over the house.

'You know low flying is dangerous, Jimmy. You ought to consider other people's feelings.' That was how she put it.

'But there have been worse marriages than ours,' he reflected. 'We don't quarrel and we respect each other.' It is doubtful what he meant by this, but it was sincere, and perhaps it meant something.

He dozed, he slept; the sun rose higher; it passed the meridian. A little sound woke the sleeper, a faint buzz, a far-away hum, and on opening his eyes he beheld an exquisitely balanced little flying machine circling in figures of eight before his face. It was a fly, the first fly he had seen, the first living thing he had seen. On the previous day he had scanned the sky often, but he had not once seen a bird.

'Perhaps the next thing I shall see will be a 'plane,' he thought, watching the cruising fly. And suddenly a terrible idea jumped into his mind: that a 'plane might pass over him, or within a few miles of him, without seeing him; that, perhaps, they were already looking for him without success. There was a pistol in the 'plane which shot Very lights, but he wanted more than that: something which would mark the place for longer. He needed a beacon. Already he had crawled out from beneath the broken wing and was standing up looking about him, and anxiously he scanned the sky. A machine might come at any time. But whether the time of waiting proved short or long, a machine would certainly come looking for him in the end. Of that he felt certain.

'Think of all the people who sent out machines to search for Nobile,' he said to himself. 'I shall stay here until they come, and I must build a beacon

from where they can see it: on the top of the bluff.'
Holding his strut as a staff he began to climb the
sloping bank of earth and found his foot was better
than he had supposed possible; it would bear his
weight so long as he moved slowly, so that his fears
of a broken bone in the instep were proved ground-
less. His foot was only bruised.

Climbing, however, was slow work, and the
bluff crumbled quickly so that it was difficult to
maintain a foothold. It was composed of dark
earth, full of blackish shale: he had seen such a
formation on the moors in Yorkshire and wondered
for a moment whether here also it went with
patches of surface coal.

When at last he had gained the top, he was re-
warded by a wide view to the west, the north and
the south. Only to the east was there higher broken
ground with cliffs which must mark the foothills
leading to those mountain ranges which he had
seen capped with snow a moment before the oil-
pipe broke. To the south-west he could trace the
course of the river-bed descending into a broken
country of rocks and little kopjes. But to the north
and north-west it was flatter, and the land seemed
to run in rocky terraces or ridges which faded out
into a flatter, distant plain. This confirmed his
general impression of the country when he was flying, but he had been too low down, fighting with a
head-wind, to get an extensive view.

When he looked down into the river-bed he saw
the wrecked machine lying at his feet and realised
that it might easily be overlooked from the air. But

since if any airman did see it, he would know what had happened, he must be careful, in building his beacon, to leave the fabric of the wings and elevator in position so that it should still be recognisable as a wrecked machine from the air. He must construct his beacon from the plywood and fabric of the fuselage, and from what spruce members he could remove from the wings, without spoiling their look.

After making his plans and sitting some time on the edge of the bluff he planted his strut on the site of his beacon and began the descent, often having to cling with his hands at the slippery wall of shale to prevent himself slipping and rolling to the bottom.

That day he made six ascents, and on each carried up a bundle for his beacon strapped upon his shoulders. But before he could begin he had to work for some time with his jack-knife, untying the fabric cover of the fuselage and unscrewing the panels of plywood, which had afterwards to be split and torn up into pieces of manageable size. In the execution of this work he became so absorbed that he forgot the hunger gnawing at his belly and the pain of his crushed foot and only paused for a moment, when he was tired out and trembling, to take a draught of water and to wipe away the sweat on his forehead. While he was still working with screwdriver and hammer, jack-knife and spanner at dismembering the fuselage, he saw that the shadows had grown long and that the sun was setting.

It was dusk when he came down after carrying

up his last load and sat for a little while, too weary
to put on his night-clothes, as his flying-suit had
now become. After a little he roused himself, and,
crawling into his kennel below the wing, he sat
there with his head and shoulders pressing against
the underside of the wing, massaging his foot. He
was very hungry, but made up his mind that he
would not think of food until after he had got his
beacon built, which would take him the whole of
the next day, for he could carry very little up with
him at one time. His mind was so full of plans that
sleep did not come easily: no sooner had one problem been solved, and a course of action decided on,
than a new idea presented itself which he felt that
he must debate in his own mind. Thus his thoughts
raced, without control, in a sort of circular pattern,
until at last the problems he set himself, and the
ideas which assailed him, became irrelevant to his
situation, and when at last he fell asleep it was with
the conviction that he must remember to mark his
grave on the map which he had decided to make
in his log-book, and that he would call it *organic
remains*.

The next morning the sun was high up when he
awoke, but there was a gentle breeze which fluttered a piece of newspaper which he had left in
the cockpit. He felt weak rather than excessively
hungry, and took a large draught of water and two
tablets of cascara from the bottle which he had
slipped into his waistcoat pocket on the morning of
the flight before setting out. Then he set promptly
about the great work of loosening one of the petrol

tanks in the wing, after draining all the petrol out of it into the lower tank. When at last he had got it out he carried it up on to the bluff empty, intending afterwards to carry petrol up in small quantities until he had enough stored away, not only to set his beacon blazing quickly, but also, to make a very great flare itself, if he should need to signal again after his bonfire had burnt itself out.

That was his principal work that day, interrupted only by forced rests when he was tired, and by the calls of nature, and by two or three visits to the runnel to refill his little brandy flask with water, for he had sacrificed the thermos to the task of carrying petrol. In climbing the bluff he always used the same way and soon left a transverse line across the face of the steep bank of earth and could balance himself securely as he climbed up, even when he had the empty tank on his shoulders, though he could not put it down to rest himself.

That evening he decided to improve his shelter under the broken wing, as the wind had risen and the weather had turned colder. Indeed, the wind seemed cold enough to bring snow with it, though it was June. Perhaps this was because the wind was blowing straight off the snow mountains he had seen and the elevation was 6000 feet.

The next morning he woke up feeling better in health than he had done since he had been there, and although he still limped when he walked, his foot did not ache whenever he let it touch the ground. He did not suffer from hunger at all, though he often stopped to drink water. During the

morning he amused himself by looking over the
engine and by repairing the oil-pipe which had
caused all their trouble by coming adrift. It was an
easy matter to screw it on again.

'Who knows,' he said to himself. 'There may be
a chance of salving that engine, and it's worth a lot
of money.'

After that he busied himself in taking off the
rudder and the doors of the cockpits, intending to
use these to build the walls of his little kennel or
booth, the roof of which was the damaged wing.

In the afternoon he climbed again on to the bluff
in order to have a look-out, as it occurred to him
that perhaps a mounted party might be searching
for him in the waste. As soon as he lifted his head
over the edge of the bluff he caught sight of a big
light-brown bird of prey, an eagle or a buzzard,
which rose up from a big rock where it was perched
and flew away.

He sat for some time, motionless, on the edge
of the bluff, with his hands pressed down on the
stones, staring at the bird until it was out of sight,
his heart full of anger and savage envy that it
should fly, and that he himself was bound to the
earth, helpless. And even after the bird was gone
he remained sitting there gazing at the sky and at
the peaks of the snow mountains in the distance.
While he was transfixed thus, an idea came to him,
and suddenly he called out aloud: 'I must have a
kite!' And tumbling over this thought came the
second, that he must build himself a glider.

And without waiting to scan the plain for any

rescue party which might be seeking him, he went down the bluff as fast as he could to look again at his wrecked aeroplane and plan in his mind how the glider was to be made. But, alas, what had seemed a possible and happy way of escape, when he was sitting on the bluff, showed itself as an absurd delusion when he was once more standing beside the machine. The wing of the aeroplane was far too thick and heavy to serve for a glider, and it would need taking entirely to pieces and rebuilding with planes, saws and chisels, with glue and dope and a whole armoury of carpenter's tools, not one of which he had got. He had nothing of that sort indeed; only the tools for his engine: hammers and wrenches and screwdrivers. His only wood-working tool was his jack-knife, and he knew that he could not whittle a glider out of an aeroplane with that. He had never flown a glider, but that argument would not have deterred him if another, more powerful, had not presented itself.

'It would take me six months to build a glider with my knife, but I have no food, and unless I find food I cannot live more than a fortnight longer.'

When he had thus proved that it was not possible to make a glider he went back to his first idea, that he should make a kite.

'Anyone can make a kite,' he said to himself contemptuously. But it was some time before he could determine on its materials, for he could not find a piece of wood long enough and light enough for the spine. At last it occurred to him that he would make it of steel, and he took an oval stay

bracing-wire for the purpose. It was about eight
feet long, and he thought rigid enough.

When he had decided this and had unscrewed
the stay, he found that the sun had set, and he went
happily to rest, thinking that he would soon get his
kite made and that it would catch the eye of any
Mongolians who chanced to cross the plain.

Next morning he set to work at once on the kite,
but when he had been at work an hour he changed
his plan and decided to make a box kite. For this
he needed four stays and four cross-members to
hold them apart, and he thought that he had done
well at the end of the day when he had got the
skeleton of his kite complete, for he had had to
cut a deep notch at the end of each of his cross-
members, which would have been impossible if he
had not made them by splitting a piece of spruce,
instead of using steel.

He went to bed satisfied with himself, but exhausted, and got little rest that night. The next
morning he began to cover his kite, which took
him most of the day, because he had no needle and
could not make one. Instead of a needle he sewed
with an awl and a waxed thread, but to get the
thread he had to unpick a sewn piece of doped
aeroplane fabric, and could not often get it more
than a foot long. At the end of the day the kite was
made, and only then did he think of the string. But
there is string in plenty on every aeroplane: kite
string lacing the fabric cover on to the fuselage. He
had only to set to work to unwind it from the eyelet
hooks. Yet, when he had unwound it all, it seemed

that it would not be enough, so he began the tedious job of unwrapping the string covering of the big oil-pipe, which protects the oil from being cooled too rapidly at high altitudes.

The next morning when he got up he took his kite up to the top of the bluff, but there was no wind. The sun was already scorching hot and there was not a cloud nor a bird visible in the sky. The stones shone and dazzled him. There was no life in the desert. In the weakness which had been growing on him during the last two days he was ready to despair, and put the kite away saying to himself angrily:

'I shall not live more than another few days and I have taken so much pains for nothing, except to prove how stupid I am. And the stupidest part about it is that even if I could fly the kite, it would not do me any good. I cannot live on water much longer. I am going to croak.'

The rest of the day he did not care to look at his kite and, not being able to endure the heat of the sun, lay all day under the wing of the 'plane. The next day there was not a breath of wind stirring, and it seemed to him that his kite would never be flown at all unless someone found it and flew it after his death.

When he had drunk his breakfast allowance of water, it occurred to him that he would lose count of the days if he did not keep a diary. He therefore reckoned up the number of days that he had been in that place and wrote them down. After he had done this, it seemed clear to him that Shap and Mrs.

Beanlands had not found any natives, or if they had, then any rescue party which had set out must have turned back. They would not find him after such a long interval, but it seemed possible that aeroplanes might yet come to search, particularly if the bodies of Mrs. Beanlands and Shap had not been found.

'I must eat soon or croak!' he said in a loud voice, and, taking his log-book, wrote down: '*Latest date for food to be any good is the day after to-morrow, Wednesday.*' After this point had been settled, he took his automatic pistol and the Very light pistol, so that he could signal in case an aeroplane should come over when he was at some distance from his beacon, and set out down the bed of the river to see if he could find any signs of game. When he had walked about half a mile the river-bed became full of big boulders, and he found walking difficult, and after slipping once and hurting his bad foot, he stopped to rest, and his thoughts which had for several days been exclusively occupied by the present and the future returned to the past, and he saw vividly the aerodrome and the club-house where he had eaten his last real meal.

'Think of it: that's still going on just the same. Tug, the instructor, tired and bored to death by bad pupils, is going round on circuits all the afternoon. Mrs. Parker goes solo. Cohen needs advanced instruction. Miss Pimple has to do spins next time there's too much wind for her to do landings. What a life! What a world! Poor old Tug. If there's one thing in the world he's certain of, it's that *The Tatler* is better reading than *The Sketch*—

or *The Sketch* better than *The Tatler*. Just imagine, I've forgotten which it is! What a life! What a dull hole England is! Left-hand circuits round that aerodrome all day and a game of bridge in the club-house or a pub-crawl in the evening.

'The Groom and Horses is the spiciest place in this burg. Come along, Jimmy, we're going to investigate.'

My God, what a deadly life those fellows lead. If I do survive I hope to heaven mine will be a bit more like . . . like this.

He laughed at this strange conclusion to his thought and lifted his head, and as he did so a small hawk flew overhead, off the bluff. He fired at it at once, but his aim was not good; it is difficult in any case to shoot flying with an automatic pistol. But though he missed the hawk he was very greatly encouraged by having seen the bird, for he argued that he had now seen two birds of prey, and that there must be ground game on which they could live.

'Why are there no lizards?' he asked himself. 'That is extraordinary indeed. There should be lizards and snakes, and both can be eaten at a pinch.' From this time on his thoughts ran chiefly on hunting, and brought with them the inconvenience that he could not control the flow of his saliva and was always spitting and swallowing to be rid of it. After he had seen the hawk he came slowly back to the wrecked aeroplane, picking his way very carefully over the loose boulders for fear that he should twist his ankle again and be unable to go hunting on the morrow.

It had been a hot, absolutely windless day, but in the afternoon the wind began to blow gently from the south and it was hot in his mouth and on his skin. On the previous day such a wind would have rejoiced him, since he was thinking then only of flying his kite, but he no longer cared about it and did not bother to climb up to the bluff or to stir out of his cabin under the wing. When he did peer out the sky seemed to foreshadow a break in the weather, for it had darkened, though without any cloud showing or the sunlight diminishing. For a few moments he wondered whether it might not be the prelude to an eclipse of the sun, but he remembered that eclipses do not last much more than an hour from first to last. By five o'clock in the afternoon (by what he thought the local time) the sky had grown a strange brown colour, and he feared that a great storm was about to break out.

'I should have unfastened the whole of the other wing of the aeroplane and have carried it bodily up on to the bluff. If there is a great downpour this *wady* may fill suddenly and wash me and the 'plane itself away while I am asleep. I should have little chance in such a wild rush of waters.'

While this fear was still bothering him, and he was resolving that if it were to rain really hard it would be more sensible to sleep in the open on the bluff, the sound of a few heavy drops on the 'plane over his head startled him by their force and weight.

'It is more like hail than rain; I must see that I have not left anything in the open which will be damaged. But danger or no, I'm damned if I sleep out in a hailstorm.' And he was surprised, because the air was still hot and scorching and the wind was from the south, all of which made hail seem unlikely.

Thinking these thoughts, he began to crawl out through the little doorway he had left in his cabin (after he had walled it), and while he was on his hands and knees in the entrance he was surprised to see a big brown grasshopper just in front of him.

'Hullo, what are you doing?' he asked the insect; and quickly, before it could jump, he caught it, and, without reflecting, broke off its head while it was still looking at him, and then, pulling off the legs and wings, popped it into his mouth. It was bitter and oily, but it seemed to him good because it was food and the first solid thing he had swallowed for more than a week. All this happened while he was still on his knees in the doorway of his cabin, but as soon as he was outside he saw that the ground was covered with other grasshoppers or locusts. They were perched on the tops of the big pebbles, sitting crosswise, or on the rounded sides of them, with their heads tipping up or down, and in their folded-up state, with their round ends (their faces), they looked like large brown pocket-knives. It was queer to see so many living creatures suddenly in a place so barren. They did not jump about but sat still where they had fallen, composing themselves, and then crawling tentatively a step or two on to the top of a pebble.

The smooth upper surface of the 'plane was

dotted over with their long bodies, and he understood suddenly that what he had thought were
hailstones were really locusts. There were locusts
in the air also, falling thinly with expanded wing-
cases and feebly whirring glassy wings.

He caught another of them and mechanically
killed it, peeled it of wings and legs and chewed
it up.

'Food. They are food. I am saved,' he said, but
they were not tolerable uncooked, and he began to
catch and kill a number of the insects, killing them
by breaking their heads off with his nail and throwing their bodies into the leather case of the thermos
flask which Mrs. Beanlands had left behind. When
he had caught and killed a couple of dozen of them,
he stopped to build himself a fire with a few strips
of spruce and shreds of doped aeroplane fabric.
Over this he sprinkled a little petrol and lit it with
his cigarette-lighter. It flared up violently, wasting
itself while he sought feverishly for a steel wire on
which he threaded the locusts and held them out
to toast.

They scorched quickly; their wings burnt away
and the lower joints of their legs; then their armour-
plated bellies grew glossy and transparent with oil
and they split like little sausages, and a smell more
delicious than anything he had ever savoured came
from them. It was a smell like fish, like freshwater
fish, something like grilled trout. His mouth was
running now with sweet saliva, his eye was wet
with a big tear and his fingers shaking feverishly.
He could not wait for them to cool before he began

to eat them, and he burned himself the more since his mouth had grown unapt to hot things.

The locusts were delicious cooked, tasting like a mixture of shrimps and sausages and baked bananas. When he had toasted and eaten all that he had caught, he set to work to catch some more. He was in a frenzy and pursued them in the fury of his appetite, fearing that they might all take wing and depart suddenly. In his haste he no longer bothered to kill them cleanly, but crushed and maimed the insects by breaking off legs or head indiscriminately, and throwing the bodies rapidly on to the heap he was collecting, and pursuing them on hands and knees. At that rate it was not long before he had made himself a heap of dead and living broken bodies which would have filled a gallon measure, and with these he was content for the time, and only puzzled himself how to cook them quicker than by toasting them two or three at a time on a wire. He must roast them on a hot plate, and picking up his screwdriver and hammer he began to lever off an aluminium footplate from the top of the damaged wing, a plate which served to step on when the petrol tank was being filled. But before he had wrenched this off another idea came to him, and he unfastened a disc from one of the wheels and poured his locusts into that. Soon his fire was lighted anew and he was engaged in roasting a great mass of the insects, raking them over and over with a screwdriver as they became scorched too much on one side.

While he was eating them tears welled up con-

tinually in his eye; he was beside himself in an
ecstasy of satisfaction and impatience and he
gorged upon the food, and when they were all
gone he was not content but had to set about
catching another bagful and roasting another dish,
and these also were eaten in the same way.

By that time it was too dark for him to see to
collect any more of the insects, but for a while he
delayed going to rest and sat watching the last
embers of his fire burning away to ash. Sitting
there he fell asleep.

Half an hour later he woke up with terrible
pains in his stomach. He was sick continually, and
in such agony that he could not stifle his moans.
This lasted until nearly morning, when he was able
to feel his way across to the runnel and get himself
a drink of water and sponge the perspiration off
his forehead and wash his hands.

In this way he was taught that he must be
moderate after his fast, and although he was so
weak that he could scarcely move, he was about
directly he could see, in the first light before dawn,
collecting the sleeping locusts in bagfuls, for he
thought with terror that when the sun rose the
swarm would take wing and fly away, leaving him
with no more provision than he had before they
came. The locusts did indeed rise up and fly on,
but as other locusts began dropping soon after midday there was no great diminution in the supply.
During early morning, and in the course of the
day, he caught and killed nearly a bushel of the
insects, working until he was almost fainting with

exhaustion, but he did not eat any, since he was determined to control his appetite and diet himself until his stomach was normal.

While he was at work during the afternoon, slipping and sliding over the loose round stones, scaring the locusts to take wing at his approach, and batting them down with a piece of plywood, he rested for a moment and, looking up, saw a stream of about a dozen birds flying overhead. They travelled rapidly, and it seemed to him that they were pursuing a thin curtain of locusts, which, warping on the eastern wind, had passed over a little while before. The birds were soon out of sight behind the bluff, but Jimmy stood for some time, hoping to see them again, and watching the travelling locusts which so much resembled a travelling curtain of falling rain. During that evening and the succeeding days, he frequently saw birds of different kinds, which were following the locusts and feeding on them. Some of the birds were about the size of English starlings, but had rose-coloured breasts; the few which he saw on the ground, running about and eating locusts, seemed to be ordinary English starlings.

It gave him a great deal of pleasure whenever he saw these birds; they were evidence, he thought, that he was near the edge of the desert, but perhaps the real reason of his pleasure was because they were a familiar sort of bird, which is found near houses and in gardens and orchards, and he felt less lonely after he had seen them. The nearest he ever got to any of these birds was forty or fifty yards, and though a starling is a poor target for an automatic at that range, he would doubtless have shot at them if he had not been busy catching locusts at the time.

That evening he ate not more than a dozen roasted locusts, which tasted even more delicious than they had done the previous night, perhaps because he took a good deal more care in cooking them. After this meal he could not sleep for hunger for several hours.

Next morning he made himself a meal of forty locusts and felt no ill-effects. As the sun rose the insects took wing, and were almost all gone by ten o'clock, but other locusts began dropping all through the late afternoon. He collected another heap, and saw that with what he had got he would be saved for many days to come. But he saw also that it was no good his catching a fortnight's supply of locusts if he could not cure them and keep them from going rotten. Had he possessed either salt or vinegar, or oil, it would have been easy, but lacking all condiments he could only think of one method, viz., of parching them by roasting them as slowly as possible on a hot plate over the embers and then packing them tightly in bags.

For this purpose he sacrificed the leather seat cushions, turning them inside out. At the end of the day's work he had one cushion stuffed tight with cured locusts, and a second about a third full. He had worked hard all day and was beginning to be alarmed because he had used so much of his fuel. To economise it, he determined only to make a fire when he was curing a large number of the insects at once.

The next morning he woke early and again collected locusts, but did not get more than half a gallon. While he was gathering them he noticed many among them thrusting their tails down between the stones, and standing with their hind legs raised anxiously off the earth in the air. This attitude struck Jimmy as funny. He thought that they were relieving themselves, and they reminded him of dogs when they are about the same business.

But as soon as the sun was well up the insects were off, rising in little clouds, circling round and joining in the larger cloud which swarmed from off the bluff and circled high above the river-bed. By midday there was not a living locust to be found anywhere. During the afternoon and evening not a single insect fell in the river-bed, nor could he detect any swarms passing overhead. The locusts were gone, and Wreaks was able to wash himself all over in the runnel. He knew that he could support life for a month on what he had got, and his whole character was changed. He whistled as he splashed his naked body, and he laughed coarsely, thinking of his return to London. For the first time since their departure he began to speculate disinterestedly about Mrs. Beanlands and Commander Shap.

'Of course, he was after her money. He hated flying, but she was aching for a hero and for adventure. I guess she was brought up on Ethel Dell, and see what she came to. *The Way of an Eagle.* Not 'alf.'

Did Shap and Lily make love to each other in

the desert? Wreaks felt inclined to doubt it. 'Dear Wilmot would have been sweating with funk, if that desert is anything like it looks like. He wouldn't be feeling romantic, and, of course, poor Lily would be dog-tired, though she would be wanting love all the more. . . . It was rotten bad luck for her, and, God knows, I don't like to think of the end. . . . Of course they may be munching locusts just as I am.'

The rumblings of his gut and the calls of nature filled Wreaks with delight; they were all a proof of health and of the fact that he was going to survive. Of that he was convinced. He was a completely changed man. However, he made one discovery which upset him. As he was roasting the latest of his captures, the uncured fresh locusts, that evening he found many of them which were nearly empty. They were light; there was no substance in them. For a little while he feared that those he had cured might be the same, but he was soon reassured. The locusts he had cured were heavy; they were full of meat. He hit upon the explanation of this the next day.

While he was sitting on the shelving foot of the bluff, playing knucklebones, one of the stones chanced to fall and roll a few yards away from him, and he went after it on his hands and knees to pick it up. Beside where the stone had come to rest was one of the crouching locusts with its head crushed but its abdomen thrust into the earth. His mood was idle as he picked it up, and then he saw that there was a string issuing from its tail, and, attached to this thread, swinging in the air, a little packet much the shape of a bundle of sausages. These were clearly the eggs which the mother locust must have been in the act of laying when he had chanced to crush her with his foot.

This packet was about the size of a haricot bean, and, as he examined it, he understood the reason why some of the locusts had been so light and empty, and he guessed that the eggs would be the best part, as the roe is of fish.

He therefore began stirring the stones about on the bank and soon found other egg-packets. These he roasted for his lunch but found they were too dry, so in the afternoon he collected about half a pint more, and these he boiled in the top of the thermos flask and found them very good and tender, and a delicious change after the parched and toasted insects. It was pleasant, also, to be eating a food which did not need picking over and shelling. Eating the roasted locusts always took him some time and left the stones littered over with the remains. It was like nothing so much as eating shrimps.

For three days he lived idly, rioting in food and enjoying his new carnality. Already he was planning to set out across the desert, carrying his bags of locusts with him and a supply of water in one of the tires of the aeroplane slung round his body like a bandolier. Then one morning, when he woke up, he noticed that there was a fresh breeze blowing. This was the long-sought opportunity to fly his kite, and taking it up with a laugh, he climbed up to his beacon.

The wind was hot and southerly, and the kite lifted off the edge of the bluff and drew swiftly upwards in the up-current, and pride and joy in his kite filled him against his better judgement, for what good could the thing do him?

How it rushed upwards! How it gleamed silver against the blue! How it tugged at the string which was almost cutting into his finger! How fresh it was, how powerful, how it rode upon the air! As he watched the kite rising and falling, and growing smaller as the ball of string unrolled on the ground, he felt a lump rise in his throat. He sat down abruptly on the bluff's edge and, throwing a quick turn of the string about the calf of his leg to hold the kite, he put his hands over his face and wept out of his solitary eye. The pathos of his situation was too much; for a few moments he could not master his self-pity.

Then, without looking up at the kite, he paid out the rest of the string slowly and anchored the kite by fastening the end of it to the strut, which he thrust deeply into the ground.

'What-ho! She bumps!' he said aloud, giving the kite a defiant look. 'Someone may see that and call to inquire.'

Before six o'clock that evening the sky darkened suddenly to a coppery-brown colour, and the light seemed to throw primrose shadows on the sides of the white stones. There was the distant sound of rushing wind, of a shrill rustle which comes before a gale.

'I am in for a real storm this time,' Wreaks ex-

claimed, and started up the side of the cliff to haul
down his kite. But before he had climbed a third of
the way up a sudden flurry of locusts began to fall.
He descended again to the aeroplane in surprise,
and the weight of the strange tempest was upon
him. Down, down, down, they rained, they drove,
slowly as falling snow, thick as the thickest whirlwind of packed flakes, and the sound of their wings
was loud and shrill and more lonely than the silence
of falling snow.

His coat was covered with them in a moment; as
they struck him on his face, they scratched it with
knee and claw; he brushed them quickly off his
mouth, his ear, his eyebrow; they crunched under
his feet.

For a little while he laughed, delighted, exulting
in their numbers. He thought he would collect
enough locusts to last him six months and would
tramp back to civilisation, munching them. But
in five minutes he was exasperated by locusts, and
dived into his cabin to be out of their way. The
place was full of the insects sitting queerly about at
different angles on his clothes, with their horse-like
faces watching him, and their bent legs sticking
sharply above the line of their backs like the folding
button-hook in the pocket-knife.

He had brought a lot of them in with him on his
clothes. For five minutes he busied himself in clearing the place of them, killing them with finger and
thumb, and throwing them aside. But the number
of them in the cabin did not decrease. In the queer
yellow light, which came from the sun's light being

filtered through the million wing-cases of their fellows, they looked curiously sinister and ugly.

'Ah! you automatic beasts! Why are there so many of you?'

Wreaks looked up out of his cabin and watched them pouring down with their expanded wing-cases, their whirring wings and long dangling legs. He could hear them, the shrill sound of the whirring wings, and the little flops of those nearest to him, dropping by pure chance anywhere, as they drifted blindly on to any object in their way without making any attempt to alight gracefully. And below the sound of their whirring wings he could distinguish the persistent rustle, as they folded their wings and drew themselves up into the correct sitting posture.

Suddenly Wreaks saw that the wreck of the aeroplane was checking them as they floated down and making a drift of them. They were a foot deep all along the foot of the bluff and they were eighteen inches deep round the wheels of the 'plane. There was a locust squashing down the back of his shirt, a locust in each ear; his hair was full of them. Quickly he combed them off with his fingers, and pulled on his flying-helmet and his goggles, and, thus protected, he plunged out among them. Those drifting in the air covered him, a few hopped off him or hopped on him, but most remained where they had fallen, drawing up their legs, turning their necks, staring. One scratched his nose, one he saw sitting sphinx-like on his sleeve until it suddenly bit a piece out of the material of his cuff.

He could no longer see the sun even as a radiance in a sky which was as brown as the thickest London fog: against its dimness the descending rain of living bodies was only feebly outlined; as it grew thicker it became darker, until in the brown light it was hard to see the insects when they had fallen on the reddish-brown carpet of their fellows. A sour, dirty smell sickened him; the shrill whirring of millions of wings deafened him.

Shouting oaths, Wreaks stood by the airscrew and slashed at them. But the sound of his own curses only maddened him, and roused in him a lust for massacre and destruction which he could not gratify. What was the use of striking down a hundred when the sky was stained bronze by billions of them? An insect alighted in his open mouth as he uttered a last curse, and he spat it out, suddenly sickened.

Yet he would kill and kill, and he stood striking angrily, exhausting himself with futile blows, until suddenly a better idea occurred to him. Since the crash he had pulled the tail of the machine down to the ground-level, and the propeller swung clear of the ground, and now he pulled himself swiftly to the cockpit and thrust in the plunger to dope the engine. Then he climbed out and, using all his strength, pulled the airscrew over five times to suck in petrol and get compression. Then he climbed back into the cockpit, switched on the impeller magneto, and got the engine to fire with the inertia starter. It fired unsteadily, and jets of black fumes were shot from the exhaust, then the sound changed to a gathering roar, and that blessed sound of power was lovely after the shrill rustle of desert locusts' wings! Man was speaking and challenging Nature.

He switched on the second magneto and opened the throttle. The broken, crazy skeleton of the 'plane rocked and shuddered and stuck against the boulders on which he had propped it up. The roar of the engine rose to a tornado of sound, in which the drumming of the exhaust and the scream of the propeller tips could be distinguished. The air was sucked back and hurled backwards in a furious gale, and at each of the turns hundreds of locusts fell mown down, killed and maimed, smashed into cream, or only slightly injured, and their bodies collected in a rapidly mounting heap.

'That's the way to kill 'em. Blast them, blast them, damn them. That's the way,' he shouted, unable to hear his own voice above the engine's roar. He had left it at full throttle.

Suddenly a stone gave way, the 'plane lurched forward sideways and fell drunkenly, the airscrew caught on a boulder and was shivered into a dozen fragments, and a flame ran in a flash from the engine to the wing like a flicker of lightning, which was followed by a light *poof* just audible above the roar. Without a word Wreaks, who had been watching and exulting in the massacre from the cockpit, jumped clear of the fuselage. Swift as a hare he threw himself into his cabin under the wing and dashed out with his flying-suit, which he hurled away. The flame leapt high above the central

section of the wing; he could hear it crackle and roar up in flame over his stooped head as he dived into his cabin for the second time to retrieve his automatic and the pistol with Very lights, and a cushion full of parched locusts.

He pulled all these possessions away and stood, knee-deep in living locusts, which began to crawl up him as he stood, silently watching the destruction of all his hopes. The sun was setting; already the dusk had fallen and still the flames leapt higher and higher up, and their light was reflected in the horny eyes of millions of sun-worshippers.

As he watched the flames dancing along the fuselage and licking up from the fins of the 'plane, the locusts climbed on him unheeded until he was covered in them, clinging as thick all over him as swarming bees upon a branch.

At last he noticed them, shaking his head and waking from the contemplation of his own folly to the feeling of their teeth nipping his hair, his skin, his untrimmed savage beard, testing every part of him with a sharp nibble to find if it held the moisture for which the insects were dying.

Wildly he shook himself then, and combed the clustering ranks from head and shoulder, from back and arm, and then, dancing in the light of the last flames of the burning 'plane, gesticulating like a lunatic, he gathered up the few things which he had saved and set out to climb the bluff. Its sides were practically free of insects, and he breathed for a moment with returning sanity. But when his fingers chanced to touch on one of the locusts clustering in the bundle of clothes he was carrying, he gave a convulsive shudder so violent that he nearly lost his balance. Then he swore furiously and stumbled on again, forcing himself to keep control and to fight back the madness of horror and the fury of remorse at his own folly.

He paused by the edge of the cliff and, groping carefully, felt his way to the piled slats and shreds of plywood and doped fabric of the beacon, which was all that he had left now in the world. Putting out his hand he touched the heap and grasped a locust between thumb and forefinger. He threw it aside with a wriggle of horror which shamed his efforts at control, and then pulled out his petrol cigarette-lighter and snapped it to look. The wick caught and the feeble flame flickered and threw a light which was reflected in a thousand points: every splinter of wood and carelessly piled spar, and squarer section of three-ply, bore its clustered living freight, holding on crosswise, head up or down, hanging at every angle like the crystals of rime upon a hoar-frosted bush in England.

For a moment he was so disgusted that he was tempted to burn up these also with the flame held so near to them, but he laughed at his own folly and, drawing back, clicked down the lid extinguishing the flame.

Afterwards it was lighted again, and for a little while, like a will-o'-the-wisp, the flame searched up and down along the edge of the bluff, where scarcely any insects were roosting for the night, the majority having fallen down to join the ghastly drift below, or floated a few yards farther on to the level of the plain.

The few locusts he found, Wreaks swept away with his swung leather suit, which he afterwards put on before he lay down on the bare earth, gazing at the last glowing embers of the 'plane beneath him.

In the morning when he woke his first impression was of this dizzy height, for he had moved nearer to the brink of the cliff while he was sleeping and he was almost overhanging it when he opened his eyes.

The sun was up, and the locusts were already moving; he had been awakened indeed by one of them which had dropped with a thud and scratch upon his cheek. He rolled back from the cliff and turned his head, and from the piled sticks of his beacon he saw a few insects rise on whirring transparent wings and circle, and heard also the stridulating music, their morning prayer, the first anthem of their Lord the Sun-god.

The sound came very faintly to his ears; he sat up and pulled off his leather helmet, and at once the anthem pealed louder, louder, and with a shout he sprang to his feet and, standing rigidly, he listened.

The voice which had caught his ear had dwindled, but he stood motionless, refusing to believe that he might have been mistaken, or that he was mad, and searching the distant blue spaces of the sky.

As he gazed, he saw a gathering whirlwind of rising locusts that rose up in a great vortex, stain-

ing the blueness of the sky, and as he listened
the drone of a deeper stridulation struck on his
ears.

The flame of the petrol-lighter caught at the
beacon and a tongue of fire licked the live locusts
as it soared upwards—all unnecessary. The green
Very light shot into an arc of the sky and the
roar of the suddenly visible aeroplane came in
answer.

Round the bluff it swooped, banking and circling
and diving in a swift silence, and a waved arm
answered his waved salute.

'A Moth. A Moth. A bloody little Moth!' he
whispered.

The engine roared out once more and the
machine tore away across the broken rocks of the
plain. A few minutes later it was back and circled
over him again, and once more flew straight off
towards the east. 'He's got a place to land on over
there; he wants me to follow.'

Wreaks made a hasty preparation and set off a
few minutes later after it, taking with him only his
brandy flask full of water, his two pistols and a
pocketful of parched locusts.

While he was still within a few hundred yards of
where he had started, the machine returned once
more.

'Stout fellow. He doesn't mean to lose sight of
me.'

On this occasion the machine came down in a
glide to within a few feet of Wreaks, who was able
to nod and yell his comprehension to the pilot,

before he pushed open his throttle and roared away up the line of the river to the mountains in the east.

❧

Jimmy had a twelve-mile walk before he reached the cliffs and found a way up them without difficulty. While he was climbing, the 'plane came again to look for him, but after coming close to him, it turned back and disappeared over the top of the cliff.

He climbed on, and when he reached the top he found himself on a level sandy plateau stretching to the mountains. Not two hundred yards from where he stood was the Moth aeroplane with the airscrew ticking over quietly and a helmeted goggled figure climbing out. While Jimmy had been making his way over the broken country, jumping from rock to rock and running where he found a stretch of level sand, he had been happy and light-hearted, not thinking of the future in his excitement, and only laughing between his gasps for breath and repeating to himself in his excitement that he was saved.

But the sight of the slender little Moth, with its ticking airscrew, overcame him. It was too much like home. He tried to run towards it and did not know it when he stumbled and fell with weariness, but with his eye still fixed on the machine, picked himself up and tottered crazily on. His eye was full of tears; he blubbered weakly: 'My God, my God! how beautiful!'

But the 'plane was real. The engine went on ticking over as he approached, and the pilot was walking towards him. The pilot, however, was the surprise which pulled Jimmy together and saved him from an emotional breakdown. He was a Chinaman, rather a brown-skinned Chinaman, with black squint eyes, and he was laughing, making an odd, hissing noise.

'What! You are English? I thought you would be a Russian. Well, that machine is English. I learned to fly in England. I was at Cambridge.' They shook hands, and it was a moment or two before Jimmy could bring himself to let go. Once he had touched another human being he wanted to keep hold. Then he suddenly became normal, and they talked. It turned out that Jimmy had been very lucky.

Mr. Huan Lang had been flying for one of the generals of the Northern Army. 'Then peace came —an armistice—and since the General is a very enlightened man who follows science, he sent me to watch and report on the locust swarms. They were doing an immense damage to some not-far-distant cotton estates. I followed them. I followed them three hundred miles, and last night, just as I was going to say good-bye to them, I saw your 'plane burning. So this morning I came back to see if there was anyone left alive.'

But this story ends here, months before Jimmy Wreaks will stoop to unlatch the low little front-garden gate. He will push the bell of the lower maisonette, and his wife will open it. There will be a hopeless sort of smile on her pale, troubled face; and he will give her his ugly unfortunate smile and will say apologetically:

'I've been an awful long time getting back on this trip, Daphne!'

'Yes, I know, I know. That poor woman. . . . Well, aren't you coming in, Jimmy?'

'No, I just stopped in to see you for a minute and to leave my bag. . . . Now I'll go on to the 'drome. I'll be back in a couple of hours.'

'I'll slip out and get a haddock for your supper.'

'Cheerioh.'

'Cheerioh, Jimmy.'

That will not come to pass for many months, but Jimmy has stepped up on to the lower wing and has climbed into the front cockpit and has strapped himself in and waved his arm to the pilot behind.

The throttle roared wide open; the little Moth raced across the sand, and carelessly, dangerously, swung off the earth and, after a moment or two, put up her nose to climb steeply into the sky.

Steeply, oh so steeply she climbed, shooting up behind her roaring Gipsy engine into a blue, empty Chinese sky, framed by the Gobi desert on the north and the high Nan-shan ranges on the south. There was the roar of the Gipsy engine and the Moth climbing and the wind tearing at Jimmy's unprotected head, for he had forgotten to bring his helmet, and the wind was wringing tears out of his ungoggled eye.

'Christ, this Johnny is a bad pilot. He's scaring me stiff. I wish I were back with the grasshoppers.

My nerves can't stand this. I must give him a few lessons.

Oh joy, oh blessed world! They were in the sky, riding on the air, and all the groping dirtiness of earth forgotten.

❀

Where the locusts had sojourned the desert was full of living seed: under the pebbles, in every crack in the shaly friable earth, were pushed the swollen egg-pods which broke asunder after they began to stir with life in the sun's heat and gave out the little creeping maggots.

Millions upon millions of individual living beings were scattered thus to writhe feebly and die in the vast sterility of the deserts. But where the parent swarm had favoured them by chancing on better lands, they flourished on the roots of grasses and sucked the sap of plants. Growing thus they appeared in the light of the sun, to crawl and grow and hop and devastate the earth.

Then this progeny of the swarm, those which had survived, gathered up in their clans and colonies and hopping faster and ever faster in the sun's rays, they jostled each other, and from their jostling in the heat of the day was begotten further hopping until band joined band, and legion legion, and, as the army multiplied, its movements became ordered by the pressure of one rank upon the next, and while the sun was hot they marched in serried masses at random. Down in the lush valleys the ignorant cattle crunched them complacently as they gnawed away the last blades of herbage from under their lips and passed on, leaving them to bellow and perish, and, going farther, they flowed round the weary ruined men who fought them with trenches and barricades, with flame and poisoned bait.

When they fell in waterless desert places they died; where they passed they left desert; they sprouted wings and flew. Their seed sprang again in wingless armies from the earth. They had no reason and little that might be called instinct. All their movements are due to the heat of the sun. They are thermotropic.

A RABBIT
IN THE AIR

NOTES FROM A DIARY
KEPT WHILE LEARNING TO HANDLE
AN AEROPLANE

For how to the heart's cheering
The down-dugged ground-hugged grey
Hovers off, the jay-blue heavens appearing
Of pied and peeled May!
Blue-beating and hoary-glow height; or night, still higher,
With belled fire and the moth-soft Milky Way,
What by your measure is the heaven of desire,
The treasure never eyesight got, nor was ever guessed what
    for the hearing?

HOPKINS

PREFACE

THESE notes on learning to fly are the record of my personal experience. I do not think they will be any help to other beginners, but I hope they may encourage a few middle-aged persons to learn to fly and be a consolation to the pupil who is slow to learn. He is unlikely to beat my record of twenty-eight hours before the first solo flight.

I am not a good pilot, but I should not have been so slow to learn if my education had not been so interrupted. After the first three hours it was broken off for six months and then, before I was able to go solo there was another break. And here I should say that I was much further from going solo at Ipswich than I thought I was at the time.

When I began again it was with another teacher on a different kind of machine, and, while I was learning to handle it, I did not seem to be learning anything at all. As the hours rolled by, I became depressed, and finally abandoned flying, convinced that I was hopeless. But I am too fond of the air to give it up, and after three months I began again, and because of Marshall's wonderful coaching, I persevered until my first solo surprised me and encouraged me to go on and pass my tests.

But if I have been unlucky in having my lessons interrupted, I have been exceedingly lucky in my instructors, and I take this opportunity to thank them both. My friend Leslie Honour has also taught me a great deal in casual conversation.

Now I have my licence and can fly—badly, but I hope not dangerously. To those of my readers who are learning and know less than I do, I can hardly resist giving advice, and I would say:

If you feel the slightest doubt, go round again. And to my readers who may have never flown, I can only quote Blake's words:

How do you know but ev'ry Bird that cuts the airy way
Is an immense world of delight, clos'd by your senses five?

D. G.

Hilton, *November* 10, 1931

ILLUSTRATIONS

Cockpit of Mark III Bluebird   .   .   . p. 115

Cockpit of Moth   .   .   .   .   .   . p. 171

Drawings by R. A. GARNETT *from photographs*

A RABBIT

IN THE AIR

PART I

FIRST JOY-RIDE

FOR days I had been sitting stuffily indoors; it was a lovely October afternoon and Ray and I suddenly decided to go for a walk. We don't very often go for walks together, but we do occasionally.

'Which way?' she asked at the gate.

'To the right,' I answered, for a project had that instant formed in my mind: of going to the new aerodrome at Conington, looking at it, and possibly flying.

I did not speak of this intention until we were nearly there, and then very shyly. Before we reached the aerodrome, while we were crossing the fields, we saw the machine up, turning, falling on its side, diving and flattening out again. When we climbed through the hedge into the far corner of the aerodrome, they were practising landings in the centre. Again and again the machine swooped, skimmed, nearly touched the earth, and with a roar of the engine, rose again over the trees. Ray and I were excessively cautious lest the machine should land on us, and kept so close to the hedge that we were

brushing it with our coats. At last we approached
the little shed where a group of two or three young
men were standing beside a light car and one or
two motor-cycles. They were obviously the members of the club. A dog ran this way and that.

I was very much aware of my shabby middle-
aged appearance as I asked one of the young men
whether it were possible to go up. This question
was the most difficult part of flying: it was as difficult for me as it would be to ask a member of
Boodles' whether I could hire the club dining-
room for a whist-drive.

'Do they give joy-rides?' he repeated, surprised
and blushing at being asked a question. 'I don't
know. I'll ask.'

I heard the word *joy-ride* repeated, and a tall lean
man came out and said quietly that they did. The
pilot was down by this time, his pupil was climbing
out. The tall man walked to the 'plane and spoke
to the pilot and came back to say that he would
take us up when he had given another lesson, which
would last about twenty minutes.

Ray and I strolled off (very self-consciously
strolling) along the edge of a field and spent rather
an anxious time in a very lovely little forgotten
lane where the trees wept down and the autumn
leaves lay in pale golden coinage on the ground
and fluttered gently down upon our embarrassment at the great experience waiting for us.

I was rather afraid that I might die of fear,
which I thought would be a very disgraceful and
pitiable end. My obituary would read: '. . . was

lifted out of the cockpit, having succumbed to heart failure on his first flight in an aeroplane. Mr. Garnett was a man of great moral courage. . . .'

We walked round the village, past the church and back again across a meadow. I was alarmed that we should have overstayed the twenty minutes and that our chance of flying would be gone.

As we approached the shed the machine came down. It did not occur to me that perhaps the pilot had been watching the approach of two such insignificant worms as ourselves.

'I shall go first,' I said. This was not selfishness, but courage. I would not send my wife to her death before I had tried the machine myself. I walked boldly up to the aeroplane and became apologetic. The pilot flashed very blue eyes at me. He was smiling and reassuring me, as he would have done an embarrassed spinster who had asked him: would it be bothering him too much to hand her Japanese bamboo basket to her, out of the train when she had climbed on to the platform. I stepped on to the wing and got awkwardly into the cockpit beside him, giving my forehead a good unpremeditated whack on the edge of the top plane. I shut the door and bolted it awkwardly. Then I ran my finger along the weal in the roots of my hair.

The throttle roared wide open and then was closed down, the pilot waved his arm, opened the throttle, and I watched us gather speed in an uncontrolled rush across the field.

'Here goes. . . . I'm for it now.' I drew up my knees carefully lest I should touch the rudder-bar

and gripped the edge of a pigeon-hole in the dash
in front of me.

The bumpy earth died away and we were off the
field, moving suddenly into something smoother and
softer than cream and yet this something was not
silk or cream, but nothing. There was no hardness,
no bump, we went off into the smooth nothing of
the sky, riding on emptiness. I looked over the
edge at once and the wind took hold of my hair by
the roots and pulled it hard. The hedge rushed to
us: we were going to clear it easily, we were above
it, we were soaring up freely into the nothing of
the sky. I was bare-headed and the welt I had
given myself with the edge of the plane felt like a
bar of ice. I looked down on the fields as though
I were looking at the bottom of a clear stream over
the side of a boat. It was extremely strange, but I
had no feeling of giddiness or fear. Instead of that
I was almost shouting with exhilaration.

A month before, looking down from the tower
of Lavenham church at the long back of the nave
and at the tombstones in the grass, I had felt such
nausea of terror that I could scarcely move hand
or foot. When I had lifted my eyes I was still dizzy
and sick with the knowledge that I was high over
the churchyard and that only a few feet of ancient
stone kept me from a vertical plunge to destruction. Even now when I think of it I feel sick, but
flying was different. I was almost shouting as we
flew towards Hilton. Below me the fields of stubble
had been brushed and combed with horse-rakes
and tedders until they were better groomed than

French schoolboys leaving the barber's shop. The
tidiness was incredible. I could scarcely believe
that a few agricultural labourers kept the whole
surface of the earth so well cared for. The wheat
had grown in straight rows. The whole of a thirty-
acre field had sprouted in tiny parallel straight
lines: the earth was a copper-plate engraving.

'On . . . On . . . Go on.' The engine hammered
and roared and I urged it forward with my will.
There was no sense of speed: only the song of the
engine made me believe we were moving. For a
few seconds I forgot the earth and looked about me
in the cockpit. Then I saw we were over Hilton,
crossing the end of the long narrow green shut in
by trees. It was very small. When we were over
the Manor Farm I began to speak and explain.
The stick went forward: we were descending. I
pointed: 'That's my house.' The pilot nodded,
and we began to tip up and turn over the elms,
swinging out against the air and our nose dipped
steeply.

I was lying on my side and looking down one of
the chimneys. That thin, narrow-gutted misery of
a toy was our house, about which we moved like
lethargic bluebottles from room to room! Still we
turned and dived and leaned out until I was lying
sideways on the wind with my head dipping forward. I gripped the side of the fuselage with all my
might.

'Let yourself go with the machine.'

That wasn't so easy. It was enough; it was more
than enough; I wasn't interested any longer, and

gazed feebly at the dovehouse as we straightened out at last over the black poplars by the pond and the engine roared out its song once more.

That was the church: that the Robinson's. Already, thank God, we were passing over the last paddocks and haystacks, and once again the great fields of brushed and tidy stubble were beneath us.

My first exhilaration had come back and the terror of the spiral dive was forgotten. Hammer, hammer, hammer, the engine roared; the wind tore my hair by the roots; my face was frozen. My scalp ached and smarted. If we went a bit faster my hair would snap off and I should be bald when we landed.

Here was a farm-house, there a poplar tree. We were over the landing-ground and went past it and then came circling and banking again, which made me grip and grin. An elm tree rose to meet us; its pale gold branches invited us to land on them, but we slipped away from it and sidled towards the hedge, and the tin roof and the drooping flag. The little dog ran about among the men. Ray was standing there looking up as we drifted almost silently over the hedge. There was the field: we lifted our head, we dropped our tail. Bump, bump, bump, and only with those bumps did I realise how coarse and rough everything was upon the earth, how smooth, silken and ethereal the empty air.

'It's like cream,' I shouted enthusiastically to the pilot, and began laboriously climbing out.

Ray rather anxiously got in. She was still in a state of mind I should never know again: the state of mind in which I had caught hold of the spar to lift myself up, exactly five minutes ago by the clock. With a roar they were off, and I smiled as I watched them rise.

Ray and I walked back talking. I talked the most of course. Ray had seen William bicycling across the lawn and Susie looking up at her. I pointed at the sky occasionally with my stick and said: 'I was just there. I crossed the green there and began turning there.'

'Oh we were much nearer there,' said Ray, pointing at the sky in her turn.

SECOND JOY-RIDE

The tall ground engineer had no change when I paid him for our first trip; there was nine shillings owing out of my pound. 'We'll come back and have another flip,' I said. Five minutes before I should not have used the word.

A week or a fortnight later we walked over. The pilot took me a good deal round Elsworth. The exhilaration of flying was greater, but all the strangeness was gone: I was absolutely at home and happy except when we were banking, and that made me more uncomfortable than before. There was a good deal of wind and we bumped a bit, but I liked that. Only the banks were beastly and the wind made us rock on them.

I had been watching the stick a lot and was full of notions. The ground engineer gave us pamphlets about the Flying Club. Already I knew that I should have to learn, but I was hanging back, trying to be reasonable.

In London I bought *Learning to Fly* by Swoffer, and sat practising the movements with a croquet stick in my arm-chair.

A month later I joined the club.

FIRST LESSON

DECEMBER 16TH, MONDAY, 1929

It was a lovely December morning with white frost and hardly any wind. There was a blue sky and blackbirds were singing. Soon after eleven Clayton came over the house and wagged his tail at me and I walked over the fields to Conington. A vision of a shot bird lying with a broken wing, white feathers, blood, and a gleam of bone on the frosty grass was very clear in my mind. I smiled because I could not visualise my own body in the same way, and passed on eagerly. The 'plane waiting for me outside the shed was like a formidable strutting bird with wings outstretched. They are more like birds on the ground than in the air, where they become sailing-boats of a new sort.

Clayton came forward very business-like: I put on my beret basque, my gloves and overcoat: the ground engineer booked the time. We climbed in.

And here I should describe the cockpit. In the Bluebird there is side-by-side seating, with, of course, dual control. Clayton sits on the right hand

COCKPIT OF BLUEBIRD

On the dashboard, from left to right, are shown: Pigeon-hole for maps, etc., R.P.M. (engine revolution counter), switches, air-speed indicator second pigeon-hole, watch, altimeter, oil-pressure gauge, bubble.

Below are shown: throttle lever, stirrups of rudder-bar, two control sticks and compass.

In the top left-hand corner is the petrol gauge (the tank is in the wing overhead) and the petrol-pipe leading down from the tank.

In the lower right-hand corner are the wires controlling the elevator. The simple method by which a backwards and forwards movement of the stick moves the elevator down or up can be divined.

Acknowledgements are gratefully tendered to the Blackburn Aeroplane & Motor Co. Ltd and I on the left. Each of us is strapped into his seat. We each have our feet on one of the twin rudder-bars, and each of us has a control stick between his knees. Clayton holds his in his right hand and I hold mine in my left, thus each of us has a free hand to rest on the knob of the throttle lever which sticks up in the middle between us. In front of us is a small wind-screen with a dash-board below it on which are grouped various instruments: an oil-pressure gauge, an engine revolution counter, an air-speed indicator and an altimeter. There is also a sort of arched spirit-level called a bubble.

At present I have been told not even to look at these instruments. I am to learn to fly by feel first and learn about the instruments later on. There is no telephone; we can communicate by shouting easily enough.

Clayton tested the engine at full throttle, waved away the chocks and took me up. I was so busy watching his exact movements that I hardly glanced outside at the fields slipping away. We climbed to 3000 feet; Clayton demonstrated controls and I took over very gingerly. He let me be for some time, only motioning occasionally with his fingers for me to put the nose down. I kept turning a little to the left as the rudder was a little out of true. All my thoughts were on the controls and I only looked over at rare intervals, and when I did was alarmed because I could recognise nothing: farms, fields, haystacks—I was lost. After a while Clayton banked the machine and I flew back with the sun in my eyes. Then he took over and demonstrated stalling: he put the nose up and moved the stick from side to side, and I felt the ailerons move more and more easily and produce less and less effect: finally, I wagged the stick from side to side: nothing happened. The machine was stalling. Down went the nose and back came the control as we dived.

After that he demonstrated gliding: 'Shut the throttle.' I slipped off my big glove so as to manipulate the knob gently.

'Put on your glove again.' This was said rather severely, and I understood the air was no place for fumbling with gloves if one was in a hurry. I put on the glove and shut the throttle. Silence fell. I pushed the stick forward. 'Now you're diving. Raise the stick.' The whirling propeller grew quieter and slower. It was hardly moving. 'You're almost stalling. Put the nose down.' I pushed the stick gently and the propeller picked up.

'That's right. That's the gliding angle. Make for that windmill.' There was a white streak ahead with buildings beside it.

'For that farm?' I asked.

'Yes, yes.' I swooped down two thousand feet or so in a long glide which seemed to be more a spiritual experience than a lesson in handling a machine. The propeller was ticking over mistily, and the engine scarcely to be heard. I swooped down, feeling my aching heart had first found peace with this new power. On and on, until everything was close and familiar.

Clayton pushed open the throttle and lifted us
again and banked so sharply and unexpectedly that
my new peace was knocked out of me sideways, and
I called out 'Jesus!' not under my breath but out
loud. These steep banks scare me. I shall never
learn to do them.

Once again I was lost as we climbed until I
saw that I was flying towards flooded meadows, a
meandering river, houses, churches and a bridge.

'St. Ives,' said Clayton. He swung us round
again and we saw the *R100* above a bank of haze,
waiting to moor on the mast at Cardington.

I glided again, and the field with the tin shed,
the white circle and a flag showed the aerodrome.
Clayton took her down in banks and side-slips
which were terrifying to me, but I forgot everything in the beauty of the landing and called out:
'Beautiful. Stick right back.' And sure enough, as
I spoke he put down our tail and we settled on
the ground so exactly like a bird alighting that it
would scarcely have surprised me if our 'plane had
folded its wings and begun pecking for worms
with its propeller.

We got out. I felt slightly deaf. My instructor
said it wasn't bad for a first lesson and gave me a
typewritten synopsis of the lessons.

I walked back along the plough-lands and across
the fields, grinning to myself. I felt fifteen years
younger and very hungry: ate a huge lunch and
had a headache all the afternoon from the cold
air.

SECOND LESSON

TUESDAY, DECEMBER 17TH

I walked over to Conington earlier, going a different way. It was a perfect morning, but the frost had been much harder and there was more haze about. When I appeared at the far side of the aerodrome they were running up the engine, which was missing occasionally.

The ground engineer lent me a helmet which was a little too small for me. Clayton went up for a test alone, flying low, charging the shed and zooming up. They had a job starting the engine from cold this morning: the oil was frozen and stiff. Clayton was in the 'plane waiting for me and I hurried with my coat and forgot my glasses in an inner pocket. When he had shown me how he took me up, I told him that I wanted them and fumbled awkwardly for several precious minutes. There was more haze than the previous day; the earth was seen through a sheet of lightly smoked glass and the horizon had disappeared under a brownish ring. When we turned into the sun all was a white radiance and the fields in front nearly invisible. I took over to fly level but Clayton signalled again and again for me to put her nose down: I was continually climbing.

After a little he told me to shut the throttle and glide, and I glided down and down and the smoked-glass fields became green and the hedges sprang into relief, and already I wondered: how soon and where?

'Open the throttle.' I pushed the knob forward and pulled back the stick: with a roar we shot forward and upward.

Clayton banked her and brought her round, and then I asked him if I might bank the machine myself. It seemed that my fear might be less if I learned to do it myself straight away.

And so it was: directly I began to put on rudder and push the stick to the side to drop a wing, I had no time to feel fear: it was difficult enough to know where the ground was and how steeply we were turning.

My difficulty was that there was no horizon that day for me to keep the nose on while turning. Sometimes it went down so we were beginning to dive spirally, sometimes it went up, but I kept on, turn after turn. My other trouble was a misunderstanding with Clayton, who expected me to turn in a complete half-circle (or possibly in a complete circle—I don't know), whereas I had only imagined turning the machine through a right-angle. I was always straightening her out too soon. However, on we went: pretty crazy, I daresay, the turns must have looked to anyone on the ground. I had only a very rough idea of how steeply to bank, whether to hold off bank or rudder or both, and I was shy of pulling back the stick on account of *spins* and what I had read of them. So the nose went up or down, and as I had also read somewhere of there being *optical illusions* I cannot be quite sure of anything except that all the time I had complete control and could straighten her out and fly away level as soon as I was allowed to: right, left, put her nose down, hold her nose up, keep on turning. I had to work hard.

I held the controls lightly while he planed her down and landed her, and all was well.

The helmet was an immense improvement on my beret of yesterday. I am not deaf and have avoided a headache. Again I felt as though I were a boy of twenty: not agog, but dignified and proud, etc. etc.

THIRD LESSON

TUESDAY, DECEMBER 31ST, 1929

It was a lovely morning after the gale and rain of the last two days and I eagerly awaited Clayton, who had said he would come over the house if all was ready for my lesson. Just before eleven we heard him coming, and saw him swoop down on us. He did two turns, side-slipping low over the elms, diving on to us over the dovehouse and lifting her over Harradine's cottage and waving. My word, he can fly.

Eleanor and I walked over across the fields, hurrying and slipping in the mud. It was clear and frosty but with a good bit of wind. The silly, foxhound puppy came with us and trundled absurdly after a hare.

As we approached, the ground engineer started up the engine. I hurried on my coat and my new helmet and climbed in after Clayton had explained that the turns were to be complete—360°. With a good turn one should get back into one's own slip-stream. We climbed in. Honour, the ground engineer, and old George stood by the chocks, Clayton opened the throttle and listened, his face serious and rather bothered. Then he switched over from one magneto to the other and the engine missed several times. Then he switched back to the right-hand magneto, still bothered.

'Perhaps the engine's got cold,' I ventured. He shook his head.

'We haven't the revs.' The ground engineer signed for him to throttle back and went and peered at the engine. Then he signed to switch off. The arch over one cylinder had broken off sheer, the leads to the plugs were dangling. We got out and examined the damage.

'Will you wait?' asked the engineer. 'It will take me half an hour or more to fit one of the cylinders from the spare engine.'

'Send it back and tell them what damned rotten engines they make,' said Clayton.

We arranged that I should come back after lunch. The whole chunk of metal had broken off on Clayton's flight over to Hilton and he hadn't noticed it, flying back, probably because he had the engine throttled back all the way and had glided into land. The revs. had fallen from about 2000 to 1500 at full throttle, as the result of one cylinder going out of action. The whole incident was a triumph for the routine thoroughness which made Clayton test the engine at full throttle each time it was started up afresh.

Eleanor and I walked back across the fields: the foxhound pup started another hare and a few rabbits, and we met Ray coming across the fields to meet us.

When we got back after lunch, Hart, an advanced pupil who had taken his A licence, had turned up and they had gone off. The sky was empty. It was cold, and we stamped about.

It grew colder still; we went on stamping about. Just before three there was the sound of the engine, and the machine appeared very high up.

'I thought they'd made a forced landing,' said the ground engineer, relieved. 'They are drifting a lot.'

They were. The machine came down in a series of admirable S turns, lower, lower, away, turn back . . . 'Too low perhaps?' I asked myself, and the ground engineer breathed: 'He's a bit short.' He had undershot a little I think, but as a matter of fact he just cleared the hedge and landed perfectly.

It was my turn. I went out and climbed in. Clayton looked very cold. I held the stick while he took her up and then I took over once more. While we were still quite low he told me to turn. I over-banked and didn't use enough rudder—we side-slipped a bit.

'Turn left . . . turn right . . .'

Most of my turns were bad, but I knew that they were bad, and it was a completely different affair from last time, though sometimes I let the nose go up too much, sometimes too far down. My worst fault was letting it go up when straightening out.

A turn of 360° takes a long while. I watched what I hoped was the horizon, holding off bank, keeping on rudder, and holding her nose up or down a bit and at last did one or two turns which weren't so bad.

Clayton throttled the engine back and *instinctively* I put the nose down to the gliding angle.

To do a gliding turn is the same, but you have to hold on bank and rudder and keep her nose down to the gliding angle. 'Turn left.' I eased over the stick and rudder and held them there, but kept most of my attention for the gliding angle. 'Now turn right.' I pushed over the rudder and the stick and we turned again. 'You have to use the controls more coarsely gliding.'

The fields were getting larger: quite close.

'Turn left again.' I obeyed. 'Straighten out.' The grass was really close now. We should land soon—but Clayton opened the throttle.

We did three long glides like that, coming right down on to the aerodrome each time. Then after the last Clayton opened the throttle and flew round the aerodrome low down.

'They can all notice the difference directly he takes over,' I said to myself. He landed us rather farther out in the field, not taking the hedge nearly so low, and we bumped a bit.

'I'll take your sister-in-law up now,' he said. Eleanor put on my helmet and they went up and away to Hilton. My lesson had lasted twenty-five minutes.

FOURTH LESSON

JANUARY 5TH, 1930

The blackbirds sing more now. It was a lovely morning with a S.S.W. wind blowing pretty hard in gusts: a blue sky, white clouds rolling along and the sound of the wind in the elms—too much wind for me to fly; moreover, it was Sunday, which is Clayton's busy day. Lots of pupils would be coming out, but I thought I would go and watch other people and see what I could learn from that.

When I had fed the pigeons, Ray and I set off over the fields, and she talked about the violent emotion which illuminates beautiful moments and objects in youth and how few writers try to convey it, and if they do try, what a mess they make of it.

When we got to the rough Ray said she would turn back, and we heard the machine up and suddenly saw it standing vertical in a loop, then another loop, and afterwards doing a couple of what I suppose were rolls. Ray said: 'You've got your helmet in your coat pocket.' And I answered: 'But I'm not going to fly to-day.'

The ground engineer saw me and came out and swung the propeller as I approached.

'There's too much wind really to teach you anything but spinning. We'll do spins,' said Clayton.

I would do spins.

'You have to learn them you know,' Clayton said, as I had not replied. I had not expected spins so soon, but pulled on my helmet, forgot to buckle it, climbed in and strapped myself in tightly.

'We have to go up above fifteen hundred feet to spin. It's dangerous.'

I could not help smiling at the word in Clayton's mouth, at finding that he knew its meaning so accurately. But, of course, only those who live with danger know it well. Spins below 1500 feet are dangerous, particularly with a frightened pupil grabbing the controls. Clayton opened the throttle and took off. I held the controls loosely. The wind struck us and heeled us over. For a little while we flew straight on and I wasn't sure whether Clayton was supposed to be flying the machine or I was, and made gentle movements of my own. When struck by a specially violent gust I pushed the stick over at once without waiting. He wagged a finger to the left so I banked, kept her turning, kept her nose on the horizon and held off bank. It was a good turn. With the wind behind, it wasn't so rough flying. We went on turning, climbing, turning. All good turns.

I looked at the instruments: we were at 3000 feet: flying had never been better. The sky was deep blue and we were in it: rare white curls of cloud were our only companions in the blue emptiness. The fields below were green and brown with streaks of silver water along the furrows. Flying had never been so much like sailing, but the spins were to come and I bared my teeth in an uneasy grin of fear.

Clayton began closing the throttle slowly. 'Now, I'm going to spin. Let go of the controls and I'll do it first. First, I shall stall her, then put on right rudder with the stick right back and she'll go over into a spin. To come out, central stick, full opposite rudder.'

He shut the throttle and kept easing the stick back, wagged it to show we were stalling. 'Stick right back into your stomach and now full right rudder.'

As the rudder came on the 'plane which had obviously been waiting to do something, without knowing quite what it was going to be, took a header over to the right and for the fraction of a second which that mad leap lasted I was very much afraid. Then I was hanging face downwards over a great roulette board, a jewelled roulette board of green fields and trees and stubble.

'Come out.' Clayton put on hard left rudder and the spin stopped magically: we dived: he lifted the nose: the engine roared: I took over and we climbed again. There was a village . . . was it Fenstanton? The river was just beyond it and St. Ives and the bridge: there were little roads winding among the houses. It must be Fen Drayton. I turned again and we were back at 3000 feet.

'Now we'll do it together and afterwards you'll do it by yourself.'

He shut the throttle and I kept her nose up: the stick came back farther and farther, right back into my stomach. I put on hard right rudder and we dived over and I was looking down, fascinated by the slowly-revolving, jewelled earth, cut up into little compartments of green and brown and red, like a great dish of *hors d'œuvres*. But I was

hardly allowed to look for more than a moment.
'Bring her out.' And we both put on full left rudder, the spin was over, we were diving, the engine
roared, we were flying level and climbing. Once
again we were up at 3000 feet.

'Now do it yourself.'

'Will you do the engine?' I asked.

'Yes, I'll look after the engine.' He closed the
throttle and I eased back the stick gently, wagged
it and brought it right home to the pit of my stomach. Then I put on full right rudder and to my
intense joy we went over instantly into that sideways header and once more I got the fascinating
glimpse of the jewelled roulette board, turning and
growing larger. I noticed it did grow larger. I did
not wait though I should have liked to, but put on
full opposite rudder, eased the stick forward and
eased it back, lifting her out of the resulting dive.
Suddenly I knew that that first spin had given me
what Ray had been talking about: that violent
emotion of fascinated wonder. I had got that for the
moment or two that I had allowed myself to let
her spin.

'How much height did we lose then?' I asked,
wondering whether I might be allowed to go on
spinning for a reasonable length of time.

'A bit over 700 feet.' I glanced at the altimeter.
It was all too true. I should not have been surprised if he had said sixty.

'You've never flown in clouds, have you?' asked
Clayton.

'No.' A dishevelled cloud was coming along on

our right-hand side, he swung the machine round
and we went after it.

'We shan't catch it,' I said to myself, but in a
few moments saw that it had no chance of escaping.
I climbed and steered and watched the cloud come,
a ragged feeble old white giant, just like all the
clouds one has run into on mountain-tops. I was
flying into it; and everything was blotted out
ahead. I glanced over the side, and could see fields
below, and realised suddenly there was no difficulty about elevation, for the sun at whom I have
so often grumbled was a patch of white radiance
in the whiteness on my right-hand side. If I kept it
in the same place I must be keeping the right
elevation. Lateral control I got by glancing over
and seeing a bit of field now and then.

The last shreds were slashed in two by our propeller: we were out in the blue sky—and that was
Hilton directly below us. We were 4000 feet or
more above my house.

'Now spin her again.' Once more he closed the
throttle and I stalled her, put on full right rudder,
and we went over sideways from the top of our
spring-board swallow dive. This final spin was the
best of all, the most fascinating; for the first time I was
able to realise how much larger the fields grew and
how fast they grew as they slowly turned below us.
But I knew that I mustn't wait as long as I should
like to do and I pushed out my left leg hard—then
pulled her out of the dive. We were flying level, but
a moment later the throttle was being shut again.

'You're not to spin now,' warned Clayton, see-

ing my astonished look at the altimeter. I nodded
and put the nose down and we glided to leeward
of the aerodrome, and came down in a series of
S gliding turns which were exciting in the rough
wind which tipped us about. My damned helmet
seemed to be working loose. If it blew off I should
never find it. I pulled at it with my free hand.
'Don't let her dive.' 'All right,' I said almost
crossly. What did a little dip matter anyway? I was
flying her beautifully, turning her beautifully, keeping her just right for the landing.

Clayton took over at about 150 feet and brought
her down, and I saw that a good deal of judgment
was needed in such a wind to land her on both
wheels and to keep her from tipping to one side
after the wheels had touched. I realised that for
some time I had been grinning from ear to ear.
Clayton grinned back, amused. I tore myself away
from the machine, but could not get rid of my grin.
I must have looked like a Cheshire cat to the other
pupils. I should be late for lunch, of course. But a
second glance at my watch showed that it was only
twelve o'clock, not one. When I had paid for half
an hour I had my receipt marked: Five minutes to
come. I had only been up twenty-five minutes!

FIFTH LESSON

MONDAY, JANUARY 6TH

At two o'clock Clayton came over and did two
perfect loops and a flick roll. It seems absurd to

speak of Clayton's flying. I know nothing, but one does not have to know much to tell that he is a born pilot and that he is first-class. He is always absolutely in tune with the machine and part of it. These loops of his were perfect closed circles: completed exactly where he started them, and that can't be easy. The first-class pilot like Clayton never strains his machine because, although he can make it do anything, he never jerks it or puts sudden violent loads on it. It is the bad rider who strains his horse's back at a jump, the bad pilot who strains his machine in a roll. And Clayton is acutely sensitive to the machine: he knows exactly what it wants to do and how to make it do anything without undue sudden stresses.

Directly I was up I felt out of touch with the machine and uneasy, wondering why I was there at all. When I turned I let the nose go down into a dive, then put on too much rudder and took too much off. After that all my turns were vile—I over-banked and side-slipped and let her nose go into a dive. This happened continually at every turn. The confounded sun made one quarter of the horizon invisible, and I was impatient and disgusted with myself and kept remedying one mistake too violently and falling into another. At 2000 feet odd Clayton said: 'Now do a spin all by yourself.' I closed the throttle, eased the stick slowly back, wagged it, made sure the machine was really stalled, and put on right rudder.

For a moment she seemed to be going over, but no sooner was I looking down on the earth than

something happened—the nose slipped away and
we were shooting off on a long slanting dive. I at
once put on opposite rudder, eased up her nose
and opened the throttle. 'Sorry.' I had missed
the earth somehow, I don't mean missed hitting
it, but missed aiming at it, and I was furious with
myself. I seemed to have funked it, but it was the
machine really that had funked it and I didn't
know why. She had refused to spin. I climbed and
turned, and climbed and turned, and did the turns
so vilely and so clumsily that Clayton lost patience
and showed me how a turn ought to be done. After
that I did one or two better turns.

'Now spin her again. Get her really stalled.'

I shut the throttle and waited until she was
stalled without a doubt and the stick was right
back. Then I put on right rudder and once more
we tumbled over, got a brief view of the earth and
went sliding off into a dive. I put on opposite
rudder at once, eased her up and started the
engine, feeling absolutely humiliated. Once again
I climbed and turned and looked over the water-
meadows, and did bad turns and turns which were
not so bad.

'Keep the stick right back all the time you are
spinning. Put it central as you come out.'

We were back now at 2000 feet, and at last the
moment came.

'Put her into a spin and do two complete turns
before you come out.' I got the machine well
stalled and was hugging the stick tightly to my
stomach when I put on right rudder and we went

over. The nose was pointing directly at the centre of the damned earth, and I kept it there with a feeling of malicious spite, conquering my terror. ... There was no pleasure, no delight, no exhilaration, only fear and determination mixed in a rather bitter cocktail.

'Now I'll show you a roll. A roll has the same movements of the controls but is horizontal, and you keep the engine on.'

I prepared for the roll with the same knitting together of my courage that I find necessary for the moment when I step under a shower bath. And then as the roll came on, it took me by surprise.

Up, up, up, went the nose of our boat, rising to the rush of an invisible wave till it pointed straight up at the blue arch of heaven. But as it rose, it also capsized: the right wing dropped away from under my elbow, and we were turning right over with Clayton underneath me in the cockpit. Then as the nose swung round and over, we were lying on our backs, upside down, looking at the sky below our lower wing and I was watching the nose begin to travel up again towards the earth. And then suddenly to my surprise we were almost right way up. The machine swung like a pendulum, but the incipient second roll was checked strongly by opposite aileron. The roll was over.

It had been remarkable and, like everything else, alarming when it started, but it was nothing like so exciting as a spin.

I was wondering whether I had got to be forced through doing a rotten flick roll myself when

Clayton closed the throttle and began gliding down. 'Let me take her down.' 'All right.' So I took her down, doing bad gliding turns, and gliding too steeply and getting her into a bad position for him to land. Then he took over, side-slipped her and brought her in. We were just going to land when he opened the throttle again. 'Look out for that mast!' I shouted not very politely; but the sun was almost in a line with it and it was hard to see.

He wasn't annoyed, though perhaps slightly surprised, and took us round again to avoid landing in a patch of surface water.

I had been in the wrong mood for the whole half-hour.

That night I had the sensation of spinning in a dream, but before I could stop the 'plane, something went wrong—and I stirred uneasily half-awake. This happened twice, just as it had in reality a few hours before. In my dream I felt the most awful fear, more than I have ever felt in the air.

SIXTH LESSON

WEDNESDAY, JANUARY 8TH, 1930

The blackbirds were singing as though it were really spring; it was a pearly-grey morning with high clouds, a S.S.W. wind and no sun.

Soon after eleven Clayton came over the house, looped and dived down close. I walked over.

'We shall do climbing turns and gliding turns to-day.'

When I was helmeted, bespectacled, warmly
wrapped up, and strapped in and had bolted the
door (all these preparations take me some time),
Clayton said: 'Each time you take off you test the
engine at full throttle and each of the mags.' We
roared our engine with throttle wide, switched off
one mag., switched it on again, switched off the
other, switched it on again and throttled back.
'Wave to show all's correct.' I waved. 'Now I want
you to take her up.'

Very carefully I opened the throttle, pushed the
stick forward a bit, gave her more throttle and
slowly eased the stick back to central. We were
racing over the grass, we still bumped and touched
occasionally. I did not mean to hurry her. Then
we were decidedly off, and I eased the stick back a
trifle and watched the little plantation of trees and
the line of elms and altered her course a wee bit
to steer between them, so that if the engine failed
there would be a field ready for us. There was a
gusty wind, I had to fly her a bit all the time and
took a firm grip of the stick. I steered for the windmill, flew over it and a little beyond and caught
sight of Papworth St. Everard. Everything was
clearer than I had expected.

'To do a climbing turn you bank and use rudder
at the same time, only you keep her nose just a trifle
above the horizon and you don't bank too steeply.'

We did one together and I flew back nearly to
Fenstanton, then I turned her again and flew back
to the windmill and beyond.

'I want you to practise the turns.' I banked her

a little, using a little rudder, then held off bank
and kept her nose up—on what I should personally
have called the horizon, but which I have been
taught is really above it. Slowly I edged the stick
back as the nose sagged, and kept her steadily turning all the while with the rudder. I watched the
sun dazzle of white radiance go past until I had
done my complete turn of 360°, then I flew straight
a little way and turned her round the other way.
All the time we were climbing gently and soon we
were at 2000 feet. Every moment or two I kept
looking over the edge and ahead, picking up land-
marks, identifying Papworth St. Everard, Kisby's
Hut, Rogue's lane, New Farm, Hilton, Conington
and the great rectangular patch of the Rough.
Thus for the first time I knew all the while exactly
where I was. At 2000 feet the wind was no longer
gusty but quite steady, and I went on doing turn
after turn in loose figures of eight, and looking out
again after each turn to pick up my bearings. At
every turn I waited patiently while the nose slowly
travelled round just above the horizon, not hurrying the turn or getting flustered, and easing the
stick back gently to keep her nose up while I held
off bank. I was slowly soaring round and round
like a buzzard completely at ease.

'Close the throttle and do gliding turns.' I
closed the throttle. My gliding turns were not so
good. I did not use the ailerons and rudder in
quite the right proportions. However, they were not
disastrously bad. When we were fairly low down,
about sixty feet or so, he told me to open the

throttle, and I lifted her and flew off with the wind
nearly behind me towards the Huntingdon-Cam-
bridge road. Then I turned back and did climbing turns, flying her straight a little way between
each turn to make up for wind drift and to get her
back between Hilton and Conington.

When I was back over Hilton I shut the throttle
again and did another long glide with continual
turns this way and that to the aerodrome.

SEVENTH LESSON

JANUARY 21ST, 1930

My flying has been held up because the ground
engineer has got a better job elsewhere. Without
a ground engineer to certify the machine, Clayton
cannot take me up. I regret that ground engineer
for I liked him and he inspired me with confidence.

To-day was lovely, with a hard white frost, but as
the morning advanced, a south wind got up and later
the dirty mist crept out from the hedges into the fields.

At eleven o'clock I heard a 'plane and Clayton
came over and waved his arm: it was a strange
machine. 'They have flown over from Hadleigh,'
I said to myself, and so it was. When I got to the
aerodrome the strange machine was strutting before the shed, the old man George and the Hadleigh ground engineer greeted me. The strange
machine was rather a tight squeeze, the strap was
different, the stick was thinner, the bubble too
high up to see distinctly.

I put my hand on Clayton's to open the throttle and felt his movements as he took her up, then I began flying at once myself. The wind was more bumpy than it has been before, the new machine more sensitive to bumps, and I was aware, all the time I was flying, of wind drift, particularly when turning. I fancied also that the nose tended to go up unless I held it down rather hard and the machine was much harder to hold on a course. It didn't seem so steady. I had to hold the stick tight with stiff muscles, which is all wrong.

After a time Clayton told me to shut the throttle when I thought I could glide into the aerodrome and get her in.

I shut the throttle and put her nose down, pointing at the aerodrome. I was gliding too steeply, I knew, but some angel kept whispering in my ear, 'If you glide in too flat you'll stall at a hundred feet.' I also kept twisting the machine about from left to right without definitely turning either to the left or right, in the hopes that this awkward wriggling would enable me to slow up the machine, which was gliding in too fast. The natural result of these imbecilities was that Clayton began to get quite annoyed. 'Keep her nose up. You've not got the gliding angle. Don't jerk her. You'll never get anywhere near it. Put your engine on.' I climbed and circled again, and looked at Hilton and turned in a large circle and was already between Elsworth and Conington—then cut my engine off again and once more came down too fast and too steep, not flying level and wriggling.

'You're not flying her straight. You'll never get anywhere. Don't jerk her. Glide at the right angle.' He became cross at my ladylike, silly flying. Clayton had taken great pains to get the flying started again—all for a poor hopeless booby. Three times I wavered and havered and wriggled in towards the aerodrome and then he took over and flew us round fast. I let go: it was lovely racing round, and I watched our shadow flying beneath us—a perfect aeroplane racing across the ploughed field. Then he steadied her, glided us very low, and—bump! bounce! A sibilant Scotch oath I didn't catch came out. Bump, bump, bump. We ran a good way and then pulled up. It was the first time I had known him make a bad landing. It was because of a chance rut. It had been a bad day. Clayton told me, rather savagely, I had been very bad and said that to-morrow he would land in a field at Hilton and pick me up there. That will be an excitement for the village. Old Sammy, the roadman, asked me to-day: 'Was that you, Sir, up there?' He wants to know what it feels like but cannot frame his question and I cannot tell him. I am getting a great reputation in the village of a most unexpected sort.

EIGHTH LESSON

JANUARY 22ND, 1930

Two 'planes came over this morning, the one on which I have had all my lessons till yesterday, and

the Hadleigh machine, but neither of them landed.
I drove round. The day was foggy with a south
wind, and more fog came down while we were
flying. We got into our former machine, thank
goodness. Clayton taxied her round and I took
her up. Straight into wind, get her moving, tail
up and throttle wide. Then we were racing across
the grass and the ditch getting nearer while I
eased the stick back a little—one last bump—if
there are many more we shall be in the rough
stuff—but we were off and I lifted her and steadied
her.

The wind began tipping us about a lot and came
in bumps, and we rose and fell and tipped up. I
had to practise approaches, to land on the white
circle. Holding her on her course was difficult all
the time. There was too much effort for me to
feel happy. I turned her and kept trying to keep
her straight with aileron or rudder, and once I let
the stick come too far back while I was trying to
keep her lateral control right against the wind.
'You'll kill yourself if you do that,' said Clayton.
There are lots of ways of killing oneself, but I
seemed intent on stalling the machine on a turn
for my next method was to let the nose come too
high up when I was coming out of a turn. I turned
to the left over the elms of Elsworth, turned again
by the black, broken mill, and again over Conington. Everywhere there seemed an awful lot of
trees. We raced round fast, and I kept wondering
where the hell we should get down if the engine
failed. There would be no turning down wind and

Elsworth seemed all trees and houses. When one feels like that one isn't flying well.

I shut the throttle and lowered the nose. 'Get her into wind first.' So my clever notions of gliding along the aerodrome hedge and turning in at about 30 feet were fortunately wiped out. I had to turn into wind, aiming at the circle, and then shut off throttle and glide in. In my first attempt I thought I had overshot for some reason when I had undershot hopelessly.

Then we did an approach together—a steady glide checked at about 20 feet. I felt the stick coming back, the grass coming closer and closer; we were in the ring, but before we touched he opened the throttle and I lifted her, peering to see if I were clearing the trees, and began the constant wrestling with the bumping and tipping of the infernal wind. One hellish bump scared me and I pushed the stick over wickedly. Round and round we went as I did one approach and then another, always wrestling with the wind. Some of the approaches were more or less on the mark. I was flying with my teeth clenched and my lips parted in a snarl and was full of fears.

'I've got her,' said Clayton, and with enormous relief I let go of the controls and looked over the edge feeling perfectly happy. For the first time that day I could feel the beauty of flying—the race round with tipping wings, looking down on the two waiting cars, a haystack, and a pen of bullocks, the lovely green lines of wheat, or was it beans, sprouting a tender green. Clayton landed very nicely. 'Shall I ever learn to land?' I asked, for I was despairing. 'I've had four hours now—shall I learn to land after another four?' It seemed impossible.

'I hope so,' he answered, amused. I talked longer with him on the ground and he cheered me up.

'It was really grim to-day,' he said. 'The bumps over the trees were wicked.' It was a really bad day for flying and that was a consolation.

MARCH 8TH

These winter mornings when I have hurried across the frostbound fields with the foxhound puppy gambolling beside me and biting at my gloves, when I have scrambled through the thorn hedges and gone hurrying on to meet Clayton waiting beside the 'plane, have been the most delightful of my life.

Now they are over. The club has been losing money and the Cambridge branch is to be closed down. The aerodrome will be once more a huge clay field, its thin grass interspersed with patches of wild garlic, and the hares will chase each other undisturbed through the March evenings. Clayton is going to-morrow. The machines have gone already and the telephone has been disconnected. If I had only joined the club six months earlier! For it seems to have been expressly designed for me and me alone. It was inconvenient and almost inaccessible except to me. Cambridge under-graduates had to drive out nine miles through twisty by-roads to have a twenty minutes' lesson. But it was exactly where I should put my private aerodrome if I were a rich man.

This morning I had a farewell flight with Clayton on the latest Bluebird demonstration machine which is touring the aerodromes of England. I don't know if the pilots who brought it had been told that the club had been kept going an extra week so that the members should all have a last joy-ride free of charge.

And so Clayton and I parted after we had been up and he had shown me the effect of the Handley-Page slots, by stalling the machine and keeping full lateral control.

Ten minutes flying at someone else's expense cheered the gloomy moment. I haven't learned to fly, and I suppose I never shall now.

PART II

I CONTINUE this diary after an interval of six months, during which the nearest I have got to flying was to lunch at the Savoy Hotel in honour of Miss Amy Johnson. When we were asked to autograph our cards for her, I fondly added 'Suffolk Flying Club' to mine, for I am a member of it now the Cambridge Club is dead. But it was only when I heard by chance that Clayton was at Hadleigh that I thought of making any further use of my membership. I wrote, and Clayton answered that the club had moved to a really fine aerodrome at Ipswich, and so, for a holiday this year, Ray and I are camping out with the children in three little tents on the coast, and I am to resume my flying.

Our tents are pitched on wiry grass. As soon as I had pitched them, a little R.A.F. seaplane came over and had a look at me, and to-day he came past again. I waved a red coat and he banked steeply and inspected us.

In the afternoon of Tuesday I drove over to the aerodrome. There was a new club-house, big hangars, and a large expanse of grass field stretching away to a distant line of oak trees low on the horizon. It was a real aerodrome.

The mechanic who had come over to Conington remembered me.

A Bluebird was standing with folded wings in front of the hangar. It was too windy to fly.

On Wednesday the wind increased, and by lunch-time flying was impossible. Thursday was rough with storms of rain, and we had a bad time in our tents.

NINTH LESSON

FRIDAY

Weather lovely—blue sky with fair amount of wind and woolly clouds.

At lunch-time we were shot up, not by Clayton but by the little R.A.F. seaplane, which came past absolutely skimming the beach. He took no notice of a waved towel, but a minute or so later we heard him coming back from Orford, about 1000 feet up, and heading straight over us. Before he reached us he dived steeply and did a perfectly-executed, very tight and exact loop. The seaplane's floats, like long Little Tich boots, added enormously to the somersault, head over heels effect. He was like a tumbler pigeon.

Next moment he was diving on us, and we stood fascinated and deafened, staring into the radial engine, and the great band of red paint on the side of the fuselage, and the head and face looking over at us.

He shot up again and was gone.

A moment or two later William said: 'Can I do a somersault in the air?' and tried his hardest to perform one—but he crashed each time though not seriously.

I went in and had tea at the club-house about 4.30.

The engineer swung the prop. We climbed in. 'Buckle your helmet or it will blow off.' Clayton taxied down to a far corner of the aerodrome from where we had a fine run to the belt of oak trees. 'Have you forgotten how to take off?'

'No . . . first get her going—then throttle wide and put her tail up and let her fly off before you lift her,' I rehearsed.

I half opened the throttle and grasping the stick with all my might, eased it forward and then pushed the throttle wide. We raced across the aerodrome. There was a bump or two, and I lifted her a little too soon—so that I put the nose down a trifle, but we were already off, flying a yard or two above the ground and then rising up to clear the trees.

For a while I flew her straight ahead, anxious and grimly determined, gripping the stick hard. I wondered why I was back in the air. The wind buffeted us. Clayton let me alone.

Slowly I began to look about me—a cornfield here, and there a house, and beyond it mudflats and water. We climbed higher and Clayton told me to turn. I had forgotten that on a right-hand turn you put the nose below the horizon and keep it down. On a left-hand turn you put the nose above the horizon and hold it there. When Clayton reminded me of this I realised suddenly that for the first time I had a really sharply-cut horizon line to fly by. I put the nose well down and banked

to the right and watched a medley of little boxes
roughly arranged in strings swing past the nose of
the machine. It was Ipswich. The dark strings of
houses straggled off into a few bright red ones, set
beside black roads and stretches of purple heather.
Below us was the fine space of the aerodrome with
its white central ring and the word: *Ipswich*. We
were between two estuaries; the broad Orwell between its wide mudflats was full of shipping running up into the heart of the town. I could see the
wash of a little tug five miles off, going down stream.
Farther from us the narrow estuary of the Deben
ran down from Woodbridge, and the sea swept
round between them in sparkling blue from Felixstowe to Bawdsey and beyond, revealing the whole
of Hollesley bay. I could see all the way to Shingle
Street and almost expected to be able to pick out
our little tents. I have never seen such a fine view
in my life and we were only 1000 feet up. To the
west the declining sun made it difficult to see far.
There was a strong west wind which made us
travel crab-fashion as we crossed it, and slowed us
down to about thirty or forty miles an hour when
we flew against it. So for the most part we kept to
windward of the aerodrome, turning over the mudflats of the Orwell and scudding down wind as I
turned, until we were over the purple heather of the
race-course.

I made one or two grim turns, then Clayton
took over to give me a demonstration.

'Don't use the stick as a lever to push the 'plane
round. When you want to start a turn just press

very faintly to that side and then just hold it and let the machine fly round the stick. You need hardly move the stick at all, you can hold it between your fingers and thumb.'

My anxious grip relaxed, and my set mouth relaxed also into a happy smile. From that moment I was at ease and happy and flew the machine with velvet fingers. The intense concentration of flying remained (the drowning man's agony is one half of learning to fly), but it was a pure pleasure. I was flying well. My only fault was that the tendency to start a turn too abruptly still remained.

'Shut the throttle,' said Clayton. I shut it and put our nose down and judged the gliding angle by the slowing prop., and then in the sudden silence did a gliding turn to the left, then to the right, and brought her down on to the aerodrome, while Clayton talked easily, coaching me, and fluent in the silence. He opened the throttle and we roared off across the aerodrome and rose once more, with turn after turn, to a thousand feet again, and once more I could see the estuaries wandering like streams of molten lead through the drossy mudflats, and the fleets of tiny vessels setting off adventurously towards the sweep of the encircling blue.

Twice again I brought the machine down in slow turning glides on to the aerodrome before Clayton took over and landed in a long held-off glide—bump—bounce—bump. A hare scudded away across the expanse of grass; a covey of partridges raised their heads. As we taxied back another hare started up.

Clayton was pleased with me and talked to me for a little before we got out. 'You can go straight on to landings.' I am to have lessons every day when flying is possible. My lesson had lasted thirty-five minutes.

TENTH LESSON

SUNDAY, AUGUST 24TH

'I want you to taxi over to the far corner of the aerodrome.' To taxi one uses the rudder for steering and always puts on opposite stick coarsely at the same time. I have got so used to applying stick and rudder in banking that pushing the stick over the wrong way feels funny.

So I taxied off feeling quite excited at doing something new. Then I brought her round into wind and flew off. I was much less concentrated and keyed up than last time and fully expected the machine to fly off and not just hit a hedge or tree. Yet it is only the third time that I have taken a machine up myself.

When we were clear of the aerodrome Clayton told me to throttle the engine back from 2000 to 1800 revs. I was henceforth to take over the engine, *i.e.* the throttle. We were about 200 feet up and he signalled a left-hand turn. So I put the nose of the machine up over the horizon, and while we turned I spared a glance for the bubble and found it just where it should be, in the middle of its arch. That meant I was using stick and rudder in the right proportions.

The wind was gusty: we rocked about a good deal. I flew back across to the race-course, did another left-hand turn, throttled back, put the nose down and glided into the aerodrome—but, of course, I glided in much too steeply and got shouted at. Then when we were 10 or 15 feet off the ground I opened up the throttle, flew up and round the aerodrome and repeated the performance. Again, again, again and again. Nearly always I glided too steeply. We were so low down that there was scarcely any of the lovely view I had seen on my last lesson. Round and round I flew, making one left-hand turn over the mudflats and one over the race-course, then closing the throttle and putting down the nose and corkscrewing down, watching the propeller spinning mistily and gliding down always too steeply. Again, again and again.

As I turned over the race-course, I saw an aeroplane in the nearest corner of the aerodrome begin to move and gather way.

It was old *UH*, the crashed machine with a wooden stick which lay waiting for repairs in the Conington aerodrome, until in the end Clayton flogged it off the ground and flew it back to Hadleigh at 400 feet. Since then it has been patched up and crashed twice by pupils in solo flights. Its exhaust pipe has been taken off and it makes, I believe, an infernal din. The sunlight made its wings

and body transparent silvery fish's fins. From above
and behind it, I watched it float off the ground like
a trout rising from the river bottom, riding up
easily in the translucent medium through which it
swam as lightly as a grayling. Perhaps an analogy
on a smaller scale will give a more lively understanding of the picture. Have you ever, Reader, as a
child lain down beside a small pool on moor or
seashore, a pool bottomed with sunlit pebbles and
many cushions of growing things, and then, while
you gazed enchanted into this little brilliant paradise, have you ever by chance seen a grey, feathery,
whiskered, translucent shape of stickleback or
shrimp or prawn? Then, while you watch you see
him leave the bottom and slowly float up towards
your large, spell-bound eye, yet with no contortions
or lashings of his tail—he quietly floats up airily
through the medium in which he lives and
breathes. If you have any recollection of such a
picture seen for the first time you will have a faint
understanding of what I felt, for so it was with me
watching for the first time an aeroplane taking off
from above. Yet for me it was far more wonderful
than the most magical of rocky pools revealing its
tiny world even to childish eyes, because for me it
was not only new but a world made by man in
which I could and indeed was free to enter and
play a part. Thus, for a few moments I experienced
the rapture of a child on whom a fairy has be-
stowed the power of adventuring into the rock
pool, becoming himself a shrimp or prawn or little
silvery fish.

My emotion lasted while I throttled back and glided down behind the departing 'plane.

ELEVENTH LESSON

WEDNESDAY, AUGUST 27TH

Yesterday the battery of the car failed and I could not get into Ipswich. To-day I took a bus. We are suddenly in the middle of a heat wave; the hottest days of the year. To-day there was a gusty south wind and a good deal of heat haze, fog-horns mooing at sea and a look as though there might be thunder later on. I was hot and bothered when I got to the aerodrome. We went out and got into *BF*. There was no taxying as we were facing into wind. I took off with a roar of the engine, a lifted tail, a rush across the soup-coloured grass of the aerodrome, and that last moment question in my mind: 'What the hell if she doesn't fly?'

The oak trees came nearer and nearer and we were above them. But no sooner was I in the air than all the sweet, good intentions I had been making in the last few days were blown to shreds by the wind. It was a vile gusty wind and we bounced in it and bumped on hard lumps of air and dropped suddenly through vacuous nothingness. So where there was a hole in the oak trees I headed for it; for we were only about 100 feet up and the bushy tops of the trees were close. Then as soon as I was three or four hundred yards from the aerodrome I throttled back the engine to

1800 revs., turned left, flew across the heather of the race-course to a row of bloody little houses, turned left again and shut off the engine. Clayton shoved it on again at once.

'You'll never get in from this height.' He shouted a good many other things at me during the next few trips round. 'You're doing shocking turns. You're side-slipping and nearly blowing me out of my seat. Use more rudder.' That was the result of my careful reading of Swoffer's *Learning to Fly*. I was taking off rudder after starting the turn.

Next time round it was: 'Don't over-bank. You'll turn her over on her back if you hit a bump.'

'You must keep that nose down on a turn.' Hell-fire! That was bitter. I had put the nose up just over the horizon *on purpose* because it was a left-hand turn. So much for my turns. For every two left-hand turns there was one approach to land and landing.

'You're gliding too fast. You're coming in too slow.'

I had learnt my last lesson with a vengeance and in this thin air (of the heat wave) was often dangerously near stalling the machine. In such thin air you have to land faster than usual. But each time I brought her down with very little or no assistance, checked her, held her level and then, bringing the stick back, put her wheels on the ground, and then Clayton opened the throttle at once and away we went. Again, again and again. Once he actually seemed satisfied with my ap-

proach to land and ostentatiously folded his arms
while I brought her down, judging the glide
exactly, and with the lentil porridge of the aerodrome in front of me, checked her, held her level
as long as I dared and then brought the stick back
to my stomach. I had made a sweet three-point
landing and we hardly bumped at all.

'Not so bad that,' said Clayton and pushed
open the throttle immediately for me to take off.
There was not a second's rest for me in that half-
hour. I was fighting a violent battle, and the cease-
less buffeting, the continual bumping of the wind
and Clayton's shouted advice made me desperate.
My blood was up and I flew savagely determined
to make the damned machine go where I wanted
and how I wanted. It wasn't so easy. The wind
came and went, the bumps chucked you up and
let you down and we drifted hellishly. All the
while I kept looking about for places where we
could get down in case of need. If the engine
had gone, it would have meant a very hurried
forced landing. Thus I always took her through a
gap in the oaks in the corner and turned her
over a good flat field. Then we came back over
the race-course or the grand stand and had a nasty
moment over some rows of houses. If Clayton
hadn't been there I should have broken my neck—
but all the same I'm not really scared of landings
now. The landings were easy compared with the
hellishness of low turns in a wind of forty miles an
hour and the machine bucketing about in patches
of thin air like a crazy horse. I forgot to say that

there was such a thick haze that one couldn't see any view, though I hadn't time to look.

TWELFTH LESSON

THURSDAY, AUGUST 28TH

The weather was as hot as yesterday and as hazy, but there wasn't as much wind, and when we went up the air wasn't nearly so bumpy. *UH*, the bogy machine, was started up and we climbed in. I turned her round and took off, and from the first moment she was no longer a bogy, but a jolly decent, handy little machine, far nicer than *ESZ* was and faster than *BE*. She has stub exhausts with no long exhaust pipes or silencers and so is rather noisy, but she has new wings, new undercarriage, new pistons.

The strain of flying low in a small circle, landing, taking off and making two low turns was not as great as yesterday. But it was a strain, not on my attention, for my concentration never relaxed, but on my judgment. Every second I was judging speed and distance, and angles of bank and glide. All this will become easier, and it becomes so very quickly and finally becomes as instinctive as driving a car, but at present it needs all my faculties. I feel a definite strain. Landing an aeroplane is a curious mixture of driving a racing car at top speed on a dangerous track and picking up moorings in a sailing dinghy in a racing tide and gusty uncertain wind.

The gliding angle was better, often a little too steep, and on at least two occasions I checked the glide about 15 feet too high up. Several times I held her level a little too long and made wheel landings, but two or three times I landed her damned well. On one occasion Clayton said: 'If you do two more landings like that I'll send you solo.' I wondered whether this was meant as a bribe or a threat. He was in a good temper—so I suppose I was flying better—but I think it was more the weather than me. He helped me more, and more usefully than yesterday, showing me how to bank and turn very slightly quite low down so as to aim at the gap in the oak trees. 'Who lives there?' I asked, noticing for the second or third time that he had waved. 'Some kids.'

Once or twice I caught sight of our tight little shadow racing like a sort of hunchbacked devil over the ground and vanishing out of sight. It brought home what one sometimes forgets—that we were in the air.

While flying round the factory I caught sight of a machine crossing over us, a good bit higher up. I pointed it out to Clayton, who hadn't noticed it, and he gazed at it until our upper plane put it out of sight. He'll see I'm turning into land, I thought, thinking he was probably coming down on the aerodrome himself.

'Another half-hour and I'll send you solo,' said Clayton, but I daresay my next half-hour will make him revise that judgment.

The odd thing is that I don't feel in the least

frightened of landings. I am afraid of doing something awful on a turn and killing myself; a stall on a turn is vividly present to my imagination, but a crash landing isn't so present to my mind. I'm not really afraid of a solo turn round the aerodrome, though perhaps it would be slightly hazardous. To-day's lesson lasted forty minutes. Counting up I see I have had six hours and a quarter altogether.

THIRTEENTH LESSON

FRIDAY, AUGUST 29TH

It was a boiling hot day. 'The hottest day for twenty years,' and we roasted on the beach at Shingle Street until we were scarlet and everything went dark before our eyes except the thousand twinkling flames of the wide road to the sun across the sea. Clayton was giving a lesson when I arrived. While I was waiting in front of the hangars, a girl drove up and settled herself on the veranda of the club-house. Clayton told me she was going solo, so he took her first for ten minutes to see whether she was safe before taking me.

'Are you ready to go solo?' asked Clayton, as I strapped myself beside him.

'I don't mind,' I said, and the words were exactly true. It was too hot to care. I taxied into the outfield, turned her and flew off. In the circuits which followed I was not keenly aware that I was flying very badly, but I simply could not concentrate on flying. I just did what I hoped was the right thing—my turns weren't dangerous, only clumsy—but my approaches to land were vile. I glided too steeply or too flat, and I checked her too high up—and I continually tried to put the stick right back far too soon, when I should have been holding her level. The stick only comes right back at the very last moment as she drops on the earth.

After half a dozen turns, during which I kept my eye on the other machine as much as I could, Clayton said angrily: 'Put the nose down at once when you throttle back the engine. You're stalling the machine.'

'Yes, I see that,' I said wearily and rather bored.

'Don't take it so damned quietly. You'll kill yourself.' But the day was too hot for me to fuss much about death. Clayton flew round and we made a model landing together. Then I took over again, but I was still dreadfully bad. After a few more landings Clayton kept the throttle shut, took over and taxied her back. 'It's only wasting your money for you to go on to-day. It's an off day. What have you been doing? Swimming a lot?'

It was too much sun I think, baking in the glare of Shingle Street beach until I was like a ripe fruit on a wall, but when I got out of the machine I was not apathetic, but completely dashed in spirits and miserable. I found the pubs were open and swallowed two Irish whiskies in tumblers of soda. On the way home I had two more whiskies and cheered up a bit and amused myself by driving the car with real precision. Driving well consoled me a bit for not being able to fly.

FOURTEENTH LESSON

SUNDAY, AUGUST 31ST. 20 MINS.

There was a sea mist and a north-westerly
wind off land. I got to the aerodrome at 10.45.
Clayton told me to get into *UH*, while he started
her up. I turned on the petrol.

'Contact,' he shouted. 'Contact,' I yelled back,
switching on the impeller magneto, which is the
left of the two switches.

'Off.' He swung the propeller round to the compression position. 'Contact.' 'Contact,' I yelled
back. He swung and the engine fired. I switched
on the other magneto at once, and he climbed in
beside me. 'Take her across.' There were some
sheep grazing in the far corner.

'How do you look after them?'

'Oh they keep out of the way if you fly over
them. They're well trained.'

'Always turn left on the ground when you turn
into wind.' I turned left and looked about to see
that we were in wind and that there were no
obstacles and no machine landing behind us. Then
I opened the throttle and flew off. In a fairly
strong wind the machine swings, and one has to
keep her straight, and this involves bank and
rudder ever so slightly while you're still on the
ground. When we were over the hangars I turned
to the Orwell estuary, turned again and flew back.
My first glide was just right, but I spoilt it by
checking too high up. Clayton put on the engine

and took her round, banking sharply about 30 feet off the ground and turning in a small circle. This suddenly gave me complete confidence. The stoical deliberation, the slow precise carefulness in the face of danger, which has been my recent mood, this was all blown out of me by that lovely low racing turn with one wing stretching down to within 15 feet of the turf, and once more I was swept away by the strength and power of the machine—marvellously strong, it would not dawdle about, but fly like a roaring comet, supple and powerful in my hands. When Clayton shut off the engine and took his hands off the stick, my hand went on controlling it, almost as his had done, and I still felt that the machine was full of confidence, brutal certainty and intention, and that it was happy and alive. The invention of dual control has produced a curious heredity in pilots. I learn from Clayton by a 'Laying on of hands,' for the feel of his hands on the stick is one of the chief things I learn. So he learnt from another pilot, who in his turn had learnt from one before him. There must be several distinct races of pilots, descended in this way of ordination from the original instructors existing when dual control first became universal. From them all of us are descended.

But Clayton had shut off the throttle, and his hands had left the stick as I put her into the glide and eased her up, listening to the 'whick, whick, whick,' of the visibly spinning propeller, and watching the earth approaching *very fast*, with a

last final rush it seemed. Then I checked her
gradually, held her, got her level, held her, held
her while she sank and put the stick back slowly,
but alas! just too late—another wheel landing but
not at all bad.

The earth approaches very fast . . . that streaming past so marvellously quick that the eye sees
only a rushing stream, a turbid liquid of clods and
stones melted to porridge to the eye. I had first
seen and wondered at that when I was just four
years old, and sat with my head lolling over the
rail of the governess cart with my eyes fixed on
the macadam road, while Shagpat, our New Forest
pony, bowled along at a smart trot of nine miles an
hour.

The lesson was only twenty minutes. I made
several good landings and came back in the
afternoon.

FIFTEENTH LESSON

AUGUST 31ST, 3 P.M. 30 MINS.

I climbed into *UH* while Clayton started her.
She fired and then stopped. Next time I opened
the throttle a little, and after she had fired she
moved a foot or two, so I throttled her back at once.
Clayton climbed in and I buzzed off into the outfield.

Taxying in an aeroplane might make anyone
seasick. It is like being in a very small boat in a
very bumpy sea, or like the worst wiggle-woggle

shaking-up machine at a world's fair. In the air I have never felt in the least sick and cannot imagine why anyone should. When I took off I fought hard to keep her from swinging. There was a lot of wind. I turned away from the houses and saw at once that we were travelling crab-ways, drifting across the field. By the Orwell I throttled back and detected the first symptom of nervous uncertainty in myself—for I was wondering whether I had throttled back enough to satisfy Clayton and was wanting to steal all the revs. that I dared. This was indecision of spirit and I squashed it deliberately, watching the dial until the hand flickered only just above the 1800 mark.

'Is that right?' I asked.

'Yes.' I was able to spare a moment or two to enjoy the feeling of drifting in a stiff wind. Then I banked and turned perfectly and knew exactly what Clayton meant by saying: 'Make her fly round the stick.' The wind was really fast, but I only pressed the stick to start the turn and just felt the pressure on it on the other side to hold off bank —and we turned exquisitely, perfectly evenly, although we were drifting all the time of course. I turned her again and flew over plantations of trees —umbrella domes with a little glade between them, and deep down under me were two little tents: a little green one and a larger white. 'That's what they see when they come over us at Shingle Street.' I turned again and the machine flew so beautifully round the stick that I almost wanted to call Clayton's attention to it. Then I shut off the engine and put down her nose. 'Too fast,' said Clayton, and I raised her till I heard the right 'whick, whick, whick,' of the propeller—and there was the ground again before me. Each time I came round almost exactly to the same spot, but each time there was some slight variation to make memorable the landing. Once I undershot, and Clayton gave us a short burst of the engine to give me an added margin of safety over the oak trees, but I should have done it myself if he had not been there. I remember the last but one of my landings most clearly, for I suddenly felt my heart beating violently as I shut the throttle. All my blood seemed to surge with that fierce double kick of the aorta. 'Now or never.' The glide was perfect. Clayton leant back, his hands far from the stick. As I checked her I felt the machine waver, so I banked her and steered her straight as I levelled her and held her, held her level, and eased back the stick. I felt we must touch, but we didn't till the stick was right back, right back in my stomach. It was a perfect three-point landing, and we were on the ground, but the wind struck us, a wheel caught a molehill, and we bounced all over the place.

'You *must* keep control when you've landed,' shouted Clayton. 'You can crash her on the ground, if you don't from the air.' But his wrath melted and he said in a rather Scotch way: 'Otherwise that was a very good landing indeed.'

And at the end came more praise.

'You've done very well indeed, for the wind is really tricky. You've been flying very well. I should send you solo now if it weren't for the wind.'

That meant he had noticed my turns. I was drunk with this praise and told him I would extend our holiday so as to fly again on Tuesday, with the chance of going solo then. Afterwards I waited to watch B.—a pupil who like myself is almost ready to go solo. He made three bumpy-looking landings and then they came in after his lesson had lasted only ten minutes. 'This damned wind,' he grumbled. 'I was to go solo if it had been a decent day.'

SIXTEENTH LESSON

TUESDAY, SEPTEMBER 2ND. 30 MINS.

Going solo is the nightmare which haunts all pupils who have done six or eight hours. In a perfect course of instruction no two pupils should meet and there should be no question of solo flying being strange or different—but when perfect confidence had grown up the pupil would be asked to go off by himself.

It was hot and I was tired when I reached the aerodrome. I had raced ten miles to be in time and I was two minutes late, but Clayton had gone off already with someone else.

'You said you'd be here at two.'

'I was by my watch—but I daresay it's wrong.' There were four minutes difference between them.

I got into the machine and took it out, flew her up and brought her round to land into wind

exactly as though Clayton wasn't there, with perfect confidence.

When the glide began a shout interrupted me.
'You're diving.'

'I know,' I answered savagely, though it was
barely true to call it a dive. After that I was rattled
and everything went badly. At first it was always
the same fault. I checked her all right and held her
level all right, but then I remained hypnotised,
wondering and waiting for the final moment to
arrive. So all my landings were wheel landings. I
was trying my hardest—yet I always waited a little
too long, and Clayton's criticism began to get on
my nerves.

However, we went round like that for half an
hour and though my landings did not improve,
they did not get worse. Oddly enough I was flying
exquisitely in the air, going round and round with
the precision of a circus pony galloping round the
ring. My turns are perfect now. I scarcely do anything. I just press the stick, hinting at my wish,
press the rudder-bar, and feeling the other side of
the stick, let her fly round. I watched the bubble all
the while on one turn and it never even trembled.
But my landings were bad. My landings weren't
good enough. I saw that for myself.

'Can I have another lesson to-day?'

'Yes; about five o'clock.'

So there was still the chance of going solo.

But I was feeling tired when I got out of the
machine.

SEVENTEENTH LESSON

TUESDAY, SEPTEMBER 2ND. 25 MINS.

Stupidly I waited in the aerodrome, watching the other pupils flying, speaking to one or two and becoming more exhausted and bored every minute, though I wasn't aware of how tired I was.

It was like hanging about in the corridor of a police court waiting while other people's cases were being dealt with and longing for one's own to be called. The same sick foreboding ran through me, underneath the surface hopefulness. But also I became so bored that it was painful to look at anything for more than a minute or two.

At last it was five o'clock and Clayton came down. I walked up to him in a dream and spoke to him: 'Will you take me now?' He looked round and I saw he was very weary. He had not got out of the machine the whole afternoon.

'When will you get your tea?' I asked. 'Would you rather take me in half an hour?'

'Yes.' So we had tea.

Clayton swung the propeller while I switched on and off and then I took the machine up. For some reason I was very worried by the wind. It seemed to me several points different if judged by the factory smoke than if judged by the wind stocking.

Really there was so little wind on the ground that it scarcely affected landing. My first landing was bad: my next better. But once again I felt myself becoming hypnotised waiting for the final moment of easing the stick back, back, right back!

Yet after each landing I was expecting Clayton to shut the throttle, open the door, climb out, and say: 'Once round by yourself.'

He didn't, and suddenly an entirely new vice sprang up and overcame me. I could no longer keep the machine going in the right direction as I came in to land. I put her into wind and glided down, but I never reached the spot at which I was aiming. One wing dropped a little and we drifted away to the left. When I first noticed this I corrected it angrily by a little right bank and rudder, but the moment I straightened out the leftward drift began again.

'I can't understand you,' shouted Clayton. 'You keep letting her drift to the left.' He was tired and disappointed with me, and I patiently stumbled on, refusing to believe in my failure. The ground came so fast, and I was so busy watching it and judging the right moment, that the right moment would slip by—and I would see the fierce ground rushing at me—I was leaving it too long—and levelling too quickly and the 'plane drifted sideways. . . . Every fault was corrected, but not as it occurred, only afterwards—I was dead, dumb, an automaton. I could not make myself wake up. It was like talking to the dentist after a tooth is out.

After twenty minutes, Clayton taxied the machine in, switched off, got out and walked away. I got out in my turn and stared after him, expecting him to come back and say good-bye. He refused to see me, talking to the mechanic and to the next pupil. Then he started for the office. I was being ignored. I was being snubbed, and stood rooted to the spot, while the fact that I had spent a fortnight on landings without learning enough to go solo slowly soaked in. Then I felt my neck get red and hot and my temper rising. That was silly, so I walked off and paid my cheque. Then I walked up to Clayton. He did not look at me.

'Good-bye,' I called to him in a loud voice. 'I'm off to-morrow.'

He started.

'Oh, I'd forgotten that. I'm so sorry I couldn't get you off.'

'I shall come back in a few weeks' time for two or three days, and if we can't do flying we must do some pub-crawls together.'

He laughed, and I turned my back and walked away, humiliated by my failure.

I was so nervously exhausted that I could scarcely drive the car, and did not go more than twenty-five miles an hour all the way to Felixstowe.

'Thank God, I've got a rest now. I shan't be flying now for several weeks. Thank God for that,' I said to myself while the Ford crawled along like a dying bluebottle. 'I couldn't have stood the strain of landings much longer. And now for a drink.' But my money hadn't come from the bank and when I had bought bread and Kodak films I only had a shilling left. The eightpence on a gin was pure waste. I needed a tumbler of it to do me any good.

PART III

M O T H S

I WENT over to Marshall's Aerodrome the other
morning telling myself that I was doing so just
out of curiosity and because I wanted to see a few
aeroplanes. But, really, I was giving way to an
irresistible impulse. I could no longer keep away.
What I found was a rough-looking large field, two
men installing a pylon-shaped petrol pump, and a
big range of hangars.

After a little the ground engineer came along
and we looked at each other curiously: he was
Honour. He showed me the two school Moths,
and we chatted. After this I saw Mr. Marshall,
jun., who is the instructor at the school, and told
him that I had come because Ipswich was too far
off and hopeless for me to get at. He told me that
even if I had finished on Bluebirds I should need
several hours instruction on Moths.

On Sunday, October 19th, I went over again to
see a three-engined Westland Wessex which was
paying a visit to the school, and when I arrived I
found not only this big monoplane but eight or
nine Moths and a Puss Moth. I also met two
members of the school whom I knew, talked to
them and ended by pushing myself forward and
going up for a joy-ride in the Puss Moth—a demonstration machine from De Havilland's. We

took off very quickly and climbed fast. With the inverted engine one gets a marvellous view and the machine is hardly noisier than a car on second gear. Directly we landed, I joined the school. I had really made up my mind to do so the moment that I had met Marshall and had only held back because of the natural reluctance to start learning on a new type of machine before mastering the old.

But I could not afford to go and live indefinitely at Ipswich.

FIRST LESSON ON MOTHS

TUESDAY, OCTOBER 21, 1930

Moths are quite different. First, there is the tiresome bother of ear-phones. My old helmet doesn't fit and the 'phones came in the wrong places. Secondly, I felt buried in the cockpit. I was always dissatisfied with the radius of vision from the Bluebird, but one could see a good deal forward because the Genet Radial engine sloped down to the nose. With the Gipsy engine one is almost blind forward, and the wretched little wind-screen is quite opaque. One can see nothing unless one cranes one's neck out and round over the side.

(Later note.—This defect of being buried in the cockpit was at the root of many of my troubles during the following winter. Marshall was the first to discover its importance and finally remedied it by giving me two cushions. It seems to be a per-

COCKPIT OF MOTH

In aft cockpit.   Over the dash : mouthpiece of speaking tube.   On the dash : above—the bubble ; below, from left to right—watch, R.P.M. (engine revolution counter), altimeter, air-speed indicator.   The oil-pressure gauge is on the extreme right and cannot be seen from this view.   The switch is outside the cockpit on the left, just forward of the corner of the wind-screen.

On the left-hand wall of the cockpit : above—the cheese-cutter ; below—the throttle lever.   The small lever beside it is an air intake setting only to be used at high altitudes—over 10,000 feet.

Under the dash : one pedal of the rudder-bar, the control stick.

Acknowledgements are gratefully tendered to the De Havilland Aircraft Co. Ltd.

sonal one because much shorter men learn happily
without cushions, in the same machine. Perhaps
the explanation is that I have a very short neck.)

When I craned my head over, the ear-phones
were blown away from my head so that I couldn't
hear a word that Marshall said. The loneliness of
being in a cockpit all by oneself I didn't mind at all.
Indeed, I prefer it. One is able to forget one's instructor altogether at times. Moreover, the advo-
cates of side-by-side seating leave out of account
the fact that it is extremely useful to be able to look
over both edges of the cockpit.

The chief difference between the Moth and the
old type of Bluebird is one of feel. The Moth feels
much lighter; it has a much steeper angle of climb
and a flatter angle of glide. The throttle is on the
left-hand side. In the Bluebird, sitting in the left-
hand seat I have always held the stick in the left
hand (I am left-handed anyway) and now I have
to change hands. There is also a so-called 'tail-
incidence lever,' or 'cheese-cutter,' which is really
a spring loading on the stick. One pulls it back on
the glide.

I was rather flurried a good deal of the half-hour
because I couldn't hear except when we were
gliding, because I could see so little and because I
lost the aerodrome at once. Marshall took her up
and I took over. My banks and turns weren't at all
grand, but I never felt that anything dangerous
might happen. There was no feeling that she might
tip too far, or put her nose too much up or down.
There was a steady wind, the sun was shining and

smoke pouring from the factory chimneys. I took
her up to 1500 feet or so, shut the throttle and did
a long glide. That was easy, and I brought her low
down over a field. When I put the engine on I had
a shock for I felt Marshall put her nose up and
did not hear him say: 'you've got her.' I did
nothing and for a moment thought we were going
to stand on our tail. It felt just like hell. Marshall
said: 'You're climbing much too steeply,' and I
put her nose down in a hurry. After that he said:
'You're not climbing steeply enough,' and showed
the climbing angle, which gave me another shiver.
It seemed twice as steep as that of a Bluebird.

Marshall landed the machine and then I took
off, took her up, did a wide circuit, lost the aerodrome, found it again, shut the throttle, forgot the
tail-incidence lever, remembered it when we were
gliding, all without correction. Marshall then told
me to land the machine. I found no difficulty
about the gliding angle. I just looked over and
judged it by the propeller spinning and by the
feel. I can feel at once if she's diving or getting near
the stall. Bringing her in to land was simple, but I
flattened out too high and didn't put the stick back
fast enough at the end so it was a wheel landing
and a big bounce. Marshall put on a spasm of
engine and settled her down. However, I had got
her into the aerodrome.

SECOND LESSON

SUNDAY, 26 OCTOBER.   HALF AN HOUR

It was a very clear day with a light N.W. wind and very cold. By four it was getting misty, and the sun was just sinking into a cloud-bank. I am going to get a new helmet, but with a pair of socks inside the top of my old one and a scarf bound tightly round my ears I heard much better. I taxied out, finding the machine more erratic on the ground than a Bluebird. But I must give up thinking about Bluebirds.

After I had taken off, everything I did was tentative and fumbling, and I flew feebly until I glided in too high and too close on my second circuit.

Marshall suddenly took over, banked sharply, shut the throttle and side-slipped off a hundred feet or so. It was the first time I had felt a Moth well handled, and it was lovely: the earth rushed up, revealing all the tender little wrinkles and the shoots of grass, the sticks of the hedge and the blades of sprouting corn: all these little things of the earth rushed to meet me and I felt love for them. They were very beautiful.

Directly he stopped the slip I took over and made the landing. Then Marshall showed the proper circuit to make. After that there was time for one more circuit. I followed Marshall exactly, a little low, just skimming over the hedge. It was cold, my face was glowing, I have a lot to learn. I am starting again from the beginning.

THIRD LESSON

2 P.M.   NOVEMBER 4.   HALF AN HOUR

I did atrociously badly and was worried, and in that terrible passive fatalistic mood. On one occasion I bounced the machine about ten feet high. Marshall kept saving our lives. In the air I was all right. The only gratifying thing is that I can hear perfectly with my new helmet.

FOURTH LESSON

3.50.   NOVEMBER 5.   40 MINUTES

The sky was clear and cloudless, the air very cold, the wind east. Marshall went round for some little while with X—— and then got out of the machine and sent him off solo. Then he came over and we flew off. After I had taken off for the third time, I suddenly caught sight of another aeroplane close behind me on the right-hand side. I instantly banked and made a low turn away to the left. He had flown off a second or two after me before I was clear of the aerodrome.

When I had turned I could not keep sight of him and was afraid he would turn for his circuit and chase me, or if he was higher up, fail to see me. I therefore made a quick circuit to get ahead of him.

On the second or third circuit after this, just after I had closed the throttle and turned in towards the aerodrome, at the moment I was pulling the cheese-cutter back to the right notch, the same machine came floating down across my bows from the left. I suppose that it was pure chance he had not blundered into me, though of course he may have been watching me. But he should not overtake on the left or cross in front of another machine. I had leisure to watch him as I glided down and my feelings towards him were too deep for words. Marshall, however, found things to say about him down the telephone.

By the time we had landed he had taken off again and I kept out of his way, without taking my eye off him, on my next circuit. This time when we had landed we saw Honour running and X——climbing out of the machine which he had taxied into the hedge. Fortunately, it was practically uninjured. Marshall jumped out and ran over to him. I was too far to hear what was said, but saw Marshall throw both his arms above his head and bring them to his sides. No gesture could have been more expressive. There was also a third 'plane out, but the pilot spent most of the time in the centre of the aerodrome fruitlessly swinging the prop. so I had no anxiety about him except to avoid landing too close to him, and that was easy.

I have, by the way, acquired a new habit of looking a good deal at the instruments when flying. Thus on a turn I often glance at the bubble, directly we are two or three hundred feet up I look at the rev. counter and throttle back to eighteen hundred and I look at the A.S.I. as we fly off and as we come in to land.

CROSS-COUNTRY

NOVEMBER 9. SUNDAY. 11.15–12.15

Last night there was not a breath of wind and a hard frost so I looked forward to a lovely clear day, but when I woke I could hear a westerly gale roaring in the elms and the air was mild.

'The wind wouldn't matter if it weren't for these low clouds,' I thought, for there were fingers of hanging mist which raced across the sky, shutting out the occasional glimpses of sun and blue sky.

At the aerodrome I told Honour that I should like to try and find my way across country to Hilton as a holiday from landings, and Marshall gave me a radiant smile and shouted: 'Anywhere you like. Go anywhere you like.'

I took off, brought the machine round about two hundred feet up, caught sight of the railway and began to follow it, looking out for the Huntingdon road on my left. I had never flown before in such bumpy weather or so rough a wind.

'What if I should feel sick?' I asked myself, for the bumps came hard and fast, throwing me up continually against my safety-belt. Holding the machine level was all that I could do. In clear air it would have been lovely, but sheets of grey vapour whirled down on me and I was lost.

'Keep my elevation by the radiance of the sun and the A.S.I. constant, and watch the bubble tor lateral control,' I said to myself as the cloud swept over us, but when it had passed I was lost and another cloud was sweeping nearer. There was nothing for it but to put the nose down and fly lower. Then I found the railway and followed it. There was still no sign of the Huntingdon road on my left. Presently, however, I saw water-flooded fields and the river and realised that we must be near Over or Long Stanton, so I bore confidently to the left and suddenly found myself coming over Fenstanton. The Leycester's dovehouse stood up in its green paddock surrounded by trees. I closed the throttle, put the machine into a glide and called out: 'This is Fenstanton,' and then flew off to Hilton, shut the throttle and glided down: 'That is my house.'

It looked very attractive: narrow-backed, ancient, hedged in by elms. The thought came quickly to me that Marshall might not like my flying too low over trees, so I put the engine on and flew over St. John's College farm and round the field which I have decided to use if I ever land a 'plane here. Then I headed for Conington. When we were over the old aerodrome Marshall said: 'Would you like to fly on top of the clouds?' 'Yes.'

I put the nose up into the grey blanket above us and in a moment we were swallowed up and flying blindly. No, not blindly after all, for there was still a radiance in the whiteness which showed where the sun was and I could judge our angle by that, by keeping the A.S.I. and the rev. counter both constant, and I watched my bubble. The sun was visible now: a disappearing coin, a silver

threepenny bit that came and went like the Cheshire cat, but always leaving its benign smile: a
focus of radiance. But better than the sun was the
A.S.I.

'If I keep it constant at 65 m.p.h. and the revs.
constant at 1800, I must be keeping the nose up
at the same angle,' I argued.

Meanwhile, the altimeter moved steadily anti-
clockwise. At about 1200 feet we came out for
a moment and I could see the blue sky above us
and we were almost blinded by the brilliant whiteness on all sides. Soon we were right out, clear of
the clouds, and I kept her climbing steadily until
we reached 4000 feet.

The scene was wonderful, like the scenery for
the 'Snow Queen': a plain of white where nothing
stirred, where no living creature would ever set
his foot, because it was really Heaven. I was in
Heaven, out of sight of, and hidden from, the
polluting earth.

As far as the eye could see, for hundreds of
square miles, stretched the crystalline solid clouds
with occasional crevasses between them. The sun
blazed with a more than terrestrial glory in an
absolutely cloudless sky, and in the distance rose
the pointed peaks of Spitzbergen.

'They at all events are real. They can't be
clouds.'

The sun wrapped us in gold and striped the
fuselage with the shadows of the struts, and keeping
it in the same position on my right, I flew with
unbounded peace and happiness over this fairy-

land, occasionally turning my head to look behind me.

After some little while, lost in ecstatic contemplation, it occurred to me that we must have left Cambridge far behind us, and a few moments later I
caught sight of some larger fissures in the ice-floe,
through one of which I could see far down, as
though at the bottom of the sea, a square field and
a long, red-tiled farm building.

I shut the throttle and put the machine into a
glide, keeping her air-speed between 60 and 70. The
cloud table was woolly now and stretched out
wisps of nauseous vapour at me, but I steered
away from these clutching fingers to the gulf
between. As we descended the air became suddenly
bumpy, we pitched and tossed and I took up again
the task of fighting to keep the machine level laterally. Below us was a great park with gold and green
and bronze trees planted in avenues and clumps.

Where is the great house? I wondered, but perhaps it was behind, under the tail, for I saw nothing of it. On my right there was a railway line
and I swerved towards it. We had left Heaven and
once more were in England. But it was impossible
to tell what part. We might be almost anywhere
south or east of Cambridge. There had been no
means of telling the direction or the strength of
the wind above the clouds.

Marshall told me to follow the railway to the
right. Flying low along it we came to a tiny station,
but there was nothing to tell us what it was.
Farther on was a town and a factory, perhaps a

brewery, belching smoke and steam from all parts
of its roof. Marshall took over the controls and
glided down and landed on a field with sheep in it.
Landing like this was a great adventure: it made
the earth more real. Then we turned and taxied
back to the far hedge. Two boys were climbing
through a gap in it and a motor-car was stopping
at the gate.

We were at Bury St. Edmunds.

Marshall climbed out and lifted the tail of the
machine round and took off. Then I took over,
and picking up the railway line again, flew along
it. Beside the railway ran a great straight road with
plantations of beeches at intervals. All the way I
was fighting the wind. Presently I saw a racing
stable and the slender figure of race-horses in a
field. I shut the throttle for a moment to say
'Newmarket.'

'Yes, right ahead.'

I turned away from possible churches and flew
over the north side of the town over a dozen racing
stables. Every paddock seemed to be marked out
with a black circle of cinders on which the young
horses were exercised. On my right I picked up
the great white grand stand and the great expanse
of Newmarket Heath. Near a church on the Newmarket road I swung away over a fen to avoid
disturbing the service and followed the road to the
aerodrome. Marshall shut the throttle and began
to say something, but I couldn't hear. He slipped
off height and landed us. I was tipsy with air when
I got out. I was really drugged with oxygen. But

my spectacles aren't good enough: I must get goggles with my lenses if I am to fly.

FIFTH LESSON

NOVEMBER 23

I had a solid hour doing circuits, but my landings were bad, bad, bad. The day was lovely, a blue sky with rooks fighting their way against an equally blustering south-west wind. The wind was tricky and the machine needed strong handling, particularly if I used too much rudder on a turn.

Yet when the hour was over I was not too depressed. My right forearm ached from fighting with the wind, and I had enjoyed flying. Jovial and incompetent, I got out. My Meyrowitz goggles, fitted with my own lenses, are a huge success and make a great difference, for my eyelids will no longer be blown inside out. N—— gave me a bit of advice.

'To make a perfect landing, just concentrate on keeping your wheels off the ground as long as you possibly can. That is the secret.'

But such secrets are, I'm afraid, no help to me. If Marshall with all his patience has not taught me yet, it is because I cannot learn.

SIXTH LESSON

DECEMBER 7. 10–11. 1 HOUR

The weather was extremely unpleasant. There was a frost, a light south wind blowing fog which,

while we were up, turned into sleet. There was
no sign of a horizon. All the time I was letting
the wheels beat me. It was filthy, cold as sin,
and at the end of the hour I was nearly crying
with vexation. Marshall's patience and never-end-
ing helpfulness are extraordinary. I really don't
know how he puts up with me on days like this.

HOLIDAY

SUNDAY, JANUARY 25

It was too rough for landings, and I had a holiday. There was a south-westerly gale and I did
an hour's cross-country flight in a new machine
lent from De Havilland's as there is something
wrong with *EH*. It was bitterly cold and my lips
turned to wooden clappers. It was lovely flying
round Hilton, the dovehouse, so square and solid
and the white pigeons circling in a flock below me.
The brilliant sunshine was extraordinary after
these months of fog and darkness. I was completely
free from worries and exulted in a mood born of
the wind, the sun and the freezing cold. But, of
course, in a way it was a wasted hour: I wasn't
learning anything. But perhaps I can't learn, so
I may as well enjoy myself.

SEVENTH LESSON

TUESDAY, JANUARY 27. 30 MINUTES. S.S.W. WIND

I spent this half-hour in a melancholy and dismal

way. Again and again, again and again I failed to
land properly. I was leaving putting the stick back
till too late, I was coming in too fast, watching the
ground and wondering when the crucial moment
was coming and then letting it slip by. I came away
in profound gloom wondering in spite of Marshall's
help and advice and encouragement whether there
was any use in a muff like myself going on. I understand so well what he tells me but for some reason
I cannot do it. After each circuit he explains and I
make a fresh resolution, but each proves unavailing
when the crucial moment comes.

EIGHTH LESSON

SUNDAY, FEBRUARY 1ST.   10–10.30

For the first time since I've been at Marshall's
I've landed the machine properly. For the first
time I seem to have got hold of the idea. The fear-
ful, almost suicidal gloom which I have felt for
several days is lightened.

It was a dull, unpleasant morning after hard
rain in the night. The sky was dirty, but at Hilton
I could see a couple of miles. At Girton I ran into
drizzle, Midsummer Common was blanketed in a
thin, white ground mist, Cambridge had never
looked more typically and unpleasantly itself. But,
to my astonishment, at the aerodrome I could see
as far as the Gogs, and, moreover, there was a
steady east wind. I took off in the new machine,
made a hurried, confused circuit too high up and

too close in. Then I got the idea. At last I had
carried out in practice what Marshall had told
me and had shown me about the glide. Because
landing seems to start very much farther back. It
isn't a question of moving the stick nearly so much
as of making the right glide. If one makes the right
glide, the right approach, one has any amount of
time. One no longer concentrates on the crucial
moment; indeed, there isn't one.

I used to be paralysed by the crucial moment.
Now I see that it is entirely a question of making
the right approach. If the glide is right then it
means that one is entering the aerodrome at the
right height and at the right speed, one checks the
glide automatically and then one just holds on until
the machine is falling floppy as one puts the stick
unhurriedly all the way back and holds it there. I
knew all this, I had been told all this, but to-day
I discovered it by doing it for myself and got the
feel of it.

All I want is practice. Practice, practice, practice, practice! And now for the real secret at the
end. The secret of landing is the glide and the
secret of the glide is to keep a uniform speed *on the
turns*. On the gliding turn one puts the nose of the
machine down as one banks so as not to lose speed
and stall, but as one comes out of the turn one is
diving. That is the moment that you must watch.
A second or two of diving throws you all out and the
glide is ruined. Thus the art of keeping a uniform
speed on your gliding turns is the real secret of landing, unflustered and unhurried in the right place.

NINTH LESSON

FEBRUARY 2ND. 2.40–3.40

Practice was not quite as satisfactory as I had hoped. I began it with a number of good landings to the encouraging remark of 'That's the stuff,' only tempered by 'You must keep her straight on the run after you land.'

Then I slowly went off and did worse and worse, but what I did badly only convinced me that yesterday's discovery was the true explanation, for my failure was precisely in manœuvring for the glide and in gliding in too fast. I am now put in complete control of the throttle. 'The only thing I've got to feel absolutely sure about is that you'll put on the engine and go round again if you are in the slightest doubt about the landing. Then you go solo.'

TENTH LESSON

SUNDAY, FEBRUARY 8. 11–12

There was a thick belt of mist reaching up to about 300 feet above ground level, but it was thin in texture. There was a frost and a fairly fresh S.E. wind and the machine was coming in just to the left of the hangars and taking off dead in line with the rifle butts.

As soon as I was in the air I was in slight diffi-culties. I kept on putting on left rudder unconsciously. I am sick and tired of the Moth rudder, which just stays on. You have to take it off. On the whole I ham-handled the machine dreadfully.

'The landings are all right: now we only want to polish up the general flying. You have made an immense improvement in landing.' On one of my take-offs I heard a sound rather like something snapping. For a moment I wondered if something had broken in the undercarriage, but we were already in the air and I soon dismissed the incident with the explanation that a clod of earth or a stone must have been thrown up off one of the spinning wheels and hit the plane.

After I had landed Marshall said: 'You hit a partridge when you took off. Look at the blood on the wing.' He switched off and we climbed out to examine the propeller. There was a scratch into the wood just behind the metal guard on the edge, a big splash of blood on the plane, a few tiny feathers still clinging to the cross-wire. 'Lucky. It might have split the propeller if it had hit anywhere except the metal guard.'

On February 9 and February 15 I had lessons in which the now habitual alternations of optimism and despair predominated, and on each occasion I pretended to myself that I was better than I was.

For the first time in my life I am feeling the emotional lacerations of the typical schoolgirl whose vanity is engaged in the impossible task of capturing teacher's admiration and regard. Hence these tears. For though I do not pretend that scalding salty drops rain down the sides of the cockpit, yet I constantly feel a chagrin which at thirty-eight more than corresponds to such a flood.

THIRTEENTH LESSON

MONDAY, FEBRUARY 16. 2.40–3.10

There was a west wind, full of flaws and bumps near the ground, a pale blue sky, weak sunlight and grey clouds coming up from the N.W. After the first circuit he said: 'Take her up to 3000 and we'll spin.'

So I took her up in a long series of turns round the aerodrome, but gradually drifted a little towards the Newmarket side. I could see miles and miles. There was a little ground mist—not much.

'Shall I do it or do you want to show me how?'

'No, carry on.'

The altimeter was at 3000. I throttled back, pulled the cheese-cutter right back and slowly held her nose up and then, when she was really stalled, pulled the stick right back into my navel. Then I put on right rudder. With the sweep and stately grandeur of a Victorian matron the slotted Moth swung downwards, spinning slowly. But even so it was not a proper spin, for one could not keep the fuselage vertical to the earth. It spun like a top wobbling round before it stops. When we had gone round about three times I gave opposite rudder and eased the stick forward a trifle. The spin stopped instantly, and pushing the cheese-cutter forward I eased her from the dive.

'Very good indeed. That was capital. Now try her to the left.'

We had plenty of height left and I repeated the spin except that, for the first time, I did a left-hand spin. The stateliness was marvellous. I suppose it was the slots which had damped out that sudden tigerish leap of the Bluebird. But in spite of that it was the greatest pleasure I have had flying for a long time now. The sense, first of power, and then of complete abandonment to the will of the machine, is wonderful. The slowly rotating earth coming towards you as you hang over it, is a precious jewel; there is a feeling of freedom which was first experienced by the revolted angels cast out of Heaven. They came down in spins. After the spins we practised steep turns in which the elevator is used to turn the machine and the rudder to keep the nose up. Then we had one more long exhilarating spin from 2000 feet and a glide down to a bad landing.

FOURTEENTH LESSON

MARCH 8

The weather was murderously cold. I am resigned now to jogging around and around like some old pony that can't learn its circus tricks.

FIFTEENTH LESSON

MARCH 25

Anything for a change, for a holiday from this fatal business of learning to land, which I shall never learn. I am sick of going round the ring to the crack of the whip and to-day the circus pony was allowed to soar like Pegasus.

'I want to fly high.' There was not very much time, but I took off, and we went up in circles climbing round the aerodrome and then swinging away towards Newmarket. There is nothing odd about a height of 4000 or 5000; the queer feeling first became perceptible about 6000 and grew as we steadily mounted to 8000. And a little over 8000 we had to come down as time was running short. Usually one isn't aware of being high above the ground when one is flying. One just looks at it below one. But at 8000 I was aware of being very high above the earth indeed. It was a cold day with a N.E. wind and a clear sky: it had been a very dry March and clouds of dust blew along the roads. Now I could see far away beyond Newmarket and Bury into East Anglia. The water in the fens was black like slate. The bitterly cold air was thin and most delicious to breathe. All around us was nothingness: it was very lonely, very lonely. There was no other aeroplane in the sky.

After I had looked intently over the edge of the cockpit at Newmarket Heath below, I was glad to pull my head in and look only at the aeroplane.

I wasn't giddy, but there was the feeling that
a mile and a half would be a long way to fall, and
that the aeroplane was terribly fragile. I spoke to
Marshall once or twice unnecessarily so as to be
sure that he was all right. I was afraid that he
might die up there and that I should not know
until after I landed. It was lovely: it was wonderful, but my God it was cold! Down in the aerodrome it felt like the tropics: it felt like midsummer
though there was a frost out of the sun and the
N.E. wind was blowing strongly. I wonder what
it's like at 20 or 30,000 feet.

SIXTEENTH LESSON

MONDAY, JULY 13. 6.30

There has been a break of three months in my
flying, due to my despairing of ever improving,
to my being busy starting a new book, and to my
being short of cash.

The sky was overcast; rainstorms succeeded
each other with occasional claps of thunder. We
got away just as it was starting to rain in earnest,
and Marshall told me to swing away from the
clouds to the S.E. and to climb. I went up to
2000 feet, out of the way of the rainstorm, and did
vertical banks. On the first occasion I did one
with Marshall. It was a real vertical bank, the
first I have ever done, with the stick back to keep
the machine turning by means of the elevator and
using top and bottom rudder alternately to sweep

her nose up and down. Lord love us! It was a *completely new* feeling: it was extraordinary and full of power. It gave me confidence and yet I had to make myself do it as I used to make myself dive off a fifteen foot board at the baths. Only diving needs more determination and courage than flying. I can't dive now: in ten years time I shan't be able to fly.

I pushed the stick right over to the left, centred it and began to pull it back, and at the same time pedalled wildly on the rudder-bar, and the rim of the horizon swept into sight, threatened to overwhelm us with a torrent of fields, and then retreated and almost disappeared as I used top rudder.

'Keep her turning fast,' said Marshall, and I pulled a little more on the stick. It was simple once I had got used to the feel of it, and I straightened out and put her into a right-hand vertical bank immediately as a change. This time I was sweeter on the controls. We had, however, lost a lot of height so we went up to 2000 again and did more vertical banks, keeping the horizon streaming steadily past until I picked up the Cambridge factory chimneys and knew that I had done a complete turn of 360°. Then I flattened out. At the end of my lesson I flew back feeling very lost. I could see Cambridge and all sorts of chimneys and pools of water, but I couldn't spot the aerodrome. Shame kept me silent, but suddenly I recognised King's College chapel and using it as a pointer found my bearings at last. My word,

what a tiny patch the aerodrome was! We were
quite high and I glided down and brought her
round into a bad amateurish landing, saved by
Marshall.

SEVENTEENTH LESSON

WEDNESDAY

The weather was beastly: it was bumpy directly
one got into the air, and the take-off run, up and
over the rise to take-off, made me wonder each
time where Marshall would try to put her down if
she conked out.

'Try one landing and if it's too difficult, do
figures of eight.'

However my landings were good. I did one good
landing after another in vile conditions, skimming
in over the hedge and landing on the slope.

EIGHTEENTH LESSON

MONDAY, JULY 20TH

Another half-hour of landing practice. There was
next to no wind. After the moment of my first take-
off, my handkerchief was whipped out of my
pocket, and I looked down on to the cornfield on
subsequent circuits hoping that I might see it.
Marshall had insisted on my sitting on two
cushions, and I was perched up with my shoulders
just over the rim of the cockpit instead of below

it. I could see twice as well as I had ever done before. As a result my landings were the best that I had ever made.

All day I had been sitting indoors, worn out by the aftermath of the cricket match: too much *pâté de foie*, too many olives, too many pints of draught audit. And then on this dull, overcast, sorrowful evening my heart rose, my skill and confidence were supreme, and I flew like a real pilot. It was all due to the cushions.

'My handkerchief blew out of my breast-pocket,' I said, as I climbed out, and simultaneously Marshall and I looked towards the tail: there it was wrapped round the fin. We were both in very good spirits.

NINETEENTH LESSON

TUESDAY, JULY 21ST

S.W. wind and very little of it. Somehow a new standard was set yesterday, and this evening I completely failed. Wheel landing followed wheel landing, and we bounced up terribly. Usually I put on engine and went straight round again, but once I undershot, and seeing that I should just get in, did not give the spasm of engine. All my thoughts were on whether we should scrape in all right and I made a bad landing, and bouncing up, left things to take care of themselves. Marshall saved us with a last effort and I asked what from.

'A complete write-off. The undercarriage and prop. for a certainty.' Such humiliation depressed

me, and feeling more suicidal than I have done
since my last lesson at Ipswich, I went round
again and made an absolutely perfect three-point
landing, dropping the machine almost stone dead
from a couple of feet above the ground. But in spite
of that, I went home feeling that I had put off the
day in which I could be trusted and that I would
do well to shoot myself.

FIRST SOLO

WEDNESDAY, JULY 22ND

I went to the aerodrome rather early, determined
to fly well. Marshall was just taking a man for his
first lesson. When that was over I pulled on my
helmet and lifted the tail of the machine round
and taxied out. On my first landing I felt Marshall
putting the stick back a fraction of a second before
I should have done, and this annoyed me. Next
time round I did a bad landing. 'Engine, engine,'
came through the tube and I sighed and cursed,
opened the throttle, but not quite fully. Marshall
pushed it wide, and I saw that I had disgraced
myself already. The next landing was not perfect,
but I insisted that it would do, and brought her
down gently from the bounce while Marshall gave
a faint flick of engine.

'That would have been all right,' he said. 'But
last time . . .'

I am bored with repentance by this time. 'I
ought to be shot,' I said. Round once more. All

this time my approaches were perfection. This time I did a lovely landing. Before we taxied back for the run Marshall said: 'Well, it's only the throttle now.'

'I'll let you go solo now if you'll be responsible for any damage to the machine through being lazy with the throttle.'

'What might that run me into?' I asked.

'Well, it's not likely that you'll do more than a hundred pounds' worth of damage.'

It suddenly dawned on me that Marshall's request was the queerest thing I had ever heard of between teacher and pupil. I was overcome by stony anger with him and said: 'All right, I'll pay a hundred pounds, but that's the limit.'

'Well, will you taxi her back?'

While I turned the machine and taxied back, I did not think either of my coming solo flight or of the likelihood of smashing the machine or of hurting myself. I thought only that Marshall had behaved as I should never have expected, and that I had got to score off him. However, when I pulled up he lifted the tail round and, coming to the edge of the cockpit, said in a very friendly and charming way: 'You are absolutely O.K., but you must get it into your head that if you're not sure of your approach or your landing, you will go round again. Don't think that you have got to get down the first time round. You can take as long as you like. You have got three hours' petrol supply there.'

'What difference will not having your weight make to me?'

'You'll overshoot. Perhaps the first two times you'll find you've overshot, and then you'll put on engine and go round again.'

He stood back and I opened the throttle a trifle and bumped across the grass to the best position, turned into wind, and at once pushed the throttle wide open and put the tail up.

'Has he left any junk lying about in the front cockpit that might jam the controls?' I wondered as I raced across. The take-off was all right, but the climb was disappointing: Marshall's absence made no difference that I could see. I throttled back the engine and gave myself just a little extra height before I turned, making my circuit a trifle larger and giving myself a little more margin in case of engine failure. I turned over the cement works, flew her level, and turned again by the river, throttled down and made my approach.

'You are all alone up here, you bloody fool,' I said to myself on the circuit, but the fact really left me quite indifferent. I did not notice Marshall's absence and all I knew was that I must score off him by making a good landing. If I brooded on anything, it was on that he should have said anything so extraordinary. 'The machines must be insured. However, I can't think about that now.'

Lord God! I was too high. I mustn't get too close in. I sauntered down on a slow glide until I was abreast of the hangars, looking over the left-hand side, then I turned her, watching the A.S.I. and keeping the speed absolutely constant, and sauntered back again. I was just right as I turned

in. No, I had undershot a trifle. No matter. I shall
just do it nicely. I've plenty in hand really. Here
comes the hedge: here comes the white clover.
Flatten out gently. She's dropping. Stick back a
little. Hold on now. Hold on. Right back. Right
back. A gentle scrape sounded loud in my ears.
The skid scraped the machine to rest.

'What's the damage?' I wondered. 'How much
has my vanity cost me?' Then, to my astonishment, I realised that I hadn't smashed up the
machine after all. But of course I ought to have
gone round again. I turned the machine and
taxied in. Marshall and Honour were standing
together watching. Marshall waved and came
running up smiling.

'Well, that was rotten,' I said. 'I came in too
low, I came in too slow, and I suppose that I ought
to have gone round again.'

'It was perfect. It was a perfect approach and
a very good landing. It would have been a crime
to have gone round again. It was one of the best
first solos I've ever seen. The only thing is that
you taxied in rather fast just now.'

I got out.

'I hope you feel happier. You know, I've never
said that to anyone before. It's the first time I have
played that trick on anyone, but I had to make
you feel serious. I had to make sure you wouldn't
do a lazy landing.' I realised that he was referring
to me paying for the damage. It had been a trick!
All my indignation was wasted. But even then it
was too soon to feel grateful to him. But I was in

too happy a state of mind to do anything more than grin and book some more times.

Most people, went on Marshall, receive their instruction and go off solo with the ordinary routine course, but here and there one runs up against a pupil who gets into a groove, although everything else may be perfect. Take your case: everything was absolutely all right, nine out of ten landings perfect, but if you struck the tenth and it was a bad one, I was uncertain whether you would give engine or not.

But the strangest case of all was one of the best pupils I have ever had right from the first lesson, but he could not get enough confidence in himself for the first solo, until at last I felt something really drastic would have to be done. I arranged for him to have some instruction one morning at 8 o'clock and overnight asked Honour to put a second joy-stick in the front cockpit, loose. At 8 o'clock next morning we had two or three circuits and I explained that he was absolutely all right for his first solo. However, he was not anxious to go. 'All right,' I said, 'I shall go with you, but we will remove the dual control.' After much protesting on his part we taxied over to the hangars and I handed out the second stick, which had been hidden in the front cockpit overnight, and we proceeded to take off. I felt he had all the experience of a first solo, I could feel his feet shaking slightly on the rudder-bar. We came round and turned into land and I could see that the first effort at any rate was going to be a bad one. We bounced, I dared not touch my stick to correct it otherwise the whole show would have been given away, I yelled instructions down the tube and he seemed suddenly to wake up and realise that it was up to him to do something. On the third attempt he made a perfect landing, and we proceeded in this fashion for another half-hour. Next morning at 8 o'clock we went on with this performance and the same procedure was adopted until the third morning he was sent off solo. He has turned out a very good pilot.

Half-way home, I asked myself alone in the supercilious voice which has so often been used to me: 'Have you gone solo yet?' 'Yes.'

'Have you gone solo?'   'Y E S.'

'Have you gone solo?'   'Y E S.'

I drove fast and the wind blew my vainglory out of my mouth. But what had happened was a secret—a precious secret, and I did not mention it to Ray until she asked, half-way through dinner, how I had got on during my flying lesson.

TWENTIETH LESSON

SUNDAY, JULY 26

I did an hour of circuits and landings with Marshall. When there was anything wrong I put on engine and flew off. I have much more confidence now. Depression is what has been holding me back: a fatalistic gloom which has made me feel: 'Well, I may as well break my neck at once

if I can't learn to do anything else. I shall never
learn to fly.' Now I think I can fly and it makes
all the difference. And I have at last realised the
importance of putting on engine if I make a bad
landing. I have all my wits about me and don't
leave it to Marshall any more.

SECOND SOLO

MONDAY, JULY 27TH

All day there was a fresh, even a blustering wind
with intervals when the sunshine struck hot between
the shoulder-blades before the black clouds came
up to plunge us in darkness, or fall in driving rain.
I looked out of my window, bitterly regretful:
tricky winds come just as I need good weather for
solo flights.

When I reached the aerodrome it was pouring in
torrents and *YZ* stood disconsolately in the wet, while
Marshall and a pupil were waiting in the hangar for
the rain to stop so they could go up and do spins.

Yet when it was time for me to go up the wind
had dropped, the scene was golden in the declining
sun and everything seemed a perfect summer evening, when swallows hawk low after flies and the
sound of willow bat on ball comes occasionally
from the green. I began going round with Marshall
and did some good and some bad landings, but
always opened the throttle and flew off if there was
the least doubt. And it was on such occasions that
he seemed really pleased with me.

'Taxi me back. The long grass will soak me through.'

Directly I had left him and had turned up wind, I opened the throttle and flew off. Certainly the machine climbed faster without his weight. As I gained height, my mind was busy with possible places to come down on. Then on the circuit, the beauty of the evening made me forget my responsibilities and I looked about with a light heart at the sunlit fields and the distant hills and fens, until it was time to glide in.

The odd thing is that I do not hear the engine now except as a continuous pouring like the unheard sound of falling water near a weir. The great thing on the glide is to set the cheese-cutter exactly right, so that the machine glides almost hands off between 60 and 70. If it is set wrong, one is more liable to glide too slow or too fast. Full of last-minute anxieties, I made a perfect landing, then taxied back and looked at Marshall who waved me to go on. I flew round again, still in the golden sunlight, with the engine bubbling on, looking at the dark clouds which were building themselves high up for another storm.

This time I thought I was too low as I crossed the trees, and afraid of coming in too slow, gave a touch of engine. I was coming in nicely. . . . No, I had overshot. I flew off and suddenly the whole brilliantly lit earth beneath me turned black and became almost invisible. The black clouds were higher, the storm nearer. Should I get down before it broke in sheets of blinding spurting rain, driven by the onslaught of the gnashing howling furies of wind which would tear off my wings and hurl me down? Should I? No, my landing was bad again: the same story of nervous overshooting. Here comes the storm! I must hurry. The engine's note was no longer the peaceful rush of water, but the frenzied drumming of a suffocating man beating his knuckles upon the iron wall of the bulkhead in which he is held prisoner. But this time I made a good approach—a trifle too fast—a trifle too low—clearing the trees and the hedge nicely. Then, hold on, hold on, flatten a little, let the machine lose speed, hold the wheels off the ground, now, stick right back. All was perfect as I scraped and slid along.

I taxied back very slowly and felt the strain on my arms and nerves relax. Marshall took the wing and slewed the machine round. I switched off. Fifteen minutes solo. Quite good. The storm did not break after all, and I drove home enjoying the contented purr of the Ford engine, feeling very relaxed.

FORCED LANDING PRACTICE

TUESDAY, JULY 28. 6.35–7.5

A gusty wind blew all day, rumpling back the white undersides of the leaves, and when I reached Cambridge the wind-stocking blew gustily and Marshall said it was too wild for me to go solo. So we went off to do side-slips and forced landings, first climbing to 2000.

Where was the mouse or mole upon the earth?

For the silent dream-circling of the buzzard was my motion now as I did a long spiral glide. The wind blew in from the side as I banked the machine and took off rudder and pulled back stick and the brilliant fields and roof of church and barn rushed up. Now to the left, and I moved the stick slowly over, pressed the rudder-bar the other way, and the dreamy rush began again. Then we climbed once more and we began again. But now for a forced landing. Marshall is going to show me how.

'First pick a field and stick to it, even if you've picked a bad one. Then be sure you can get in, so overshoot.' Marshall shut the throttle and we made the approach together. When we were in our field, we flew off. After an interval, Marshall suddenly shut the throttle.

'What field have you picked?'

'I haven't picked one yet!'

A few desperate moments passed as I scanned the earth wildly. 'Well, it will have to be that one,' I said. 'The one with the haystack.' It was a rotten field, but the crop of red clover was the only possible thing I could see to land on. I turned and turned making my approach. 'We shall get in nicely.'

And coming low over the corn, we slid over the red clover into the field—opened the throttle and roared off.

Next time the throttle shut he asked: 'And where would you land now?'

'Why, straight ahead, into the aerodrome.' It was a long glide and no doubt it would have been safer to have picked a nearer field, but as it happened, I reached the aerodrome easily and comfortably. But when I have to do a forced landing in earnest, there may be no fields; I may be faced with a street, a row of elms, a gasworks, and have to make my choice of them.

HEDGE-HOPPING

AUGUST 2ND.   10.15–11

There was a north wind and the sky was grey with an overcast sky. Directly I was up, I ran into the mist and began to feel myself lost. After the first landing, I went round two or three times, keeping low all the time and landing well. Then Marshall suggested low flying since conditions were so disagreeable, and we set off. As I got abreast of Girton, Marshall told me to go lower as we were getting lost in clouds, although we were below 300 feet. So I came down low, picked up the Huntingdon road and flew along it. I held the stick forward, nosing down and towards the road to counteract the drift of the wind. It was marvellous. I was aware, because of the nearness of the earth, of the roaring machine, headlong hurtling, racing over the surface of the earth. Sometimes I brought her really very low and then as I saw trees looming up ahead, lifted her.

At Hilton, I did two turns round the house. I had no eyes for possible members of my family, but only for the elms as I roared off about twice their height.

With the wind behind us on the way back, we were going at the hell of a lick—about 120 miles an hour over the ground, so it was not long before hideous Girton heaved in view. I took her up a bit as I cut across to Chesterton. I shut off and brought her round perfectly to a good landing. 'Time for one more circuit.'

We took off all right, but over the elms the engine missed. Marshall throttled back, took over and lifted her up so steeply that I spoke my thought: 'What *are* you up to?'

He was gaining height for a conk out. Then he did a right-hand turn, shut the throttle and sang out: 'You've got her.'

I took her in and landed. I was drunk with air. I was wild, and driving home sang and shouted, full of realisation that we have found a new freedom—a new Ocean. For thousands of years we have crawled or run on the earth, or paddled across the seas, and all the while there has been this great ocean just over our heads in which at last we sail with joy. The longing for the sea: the call of the sea, one has heard of that, and that was the natural adventure in the past. But now it is a longing for the air, to go up. The air is more marvellous than any sea, it holds more beauty, more joy than any Pacific swell or South Sea lagoon.

This afternoon Marshall took the children up for their first flight. They sat on Ray's knee in the front cockpit. Ray and William went off over Hilton first and then Ray and Richard over St.

Ives. William was very much moved. He had liked it as I thought he would, and he began to explain, broke off and began again : he wanted to tell me very exactly the wonder of this great experience.

Richard had liked it too, and had seen the points of the railway line very distinctly.

A CRASH

AUGUST 4TH, 1931

I went to stay for two days at Lympne, adjoining Lympne aerodrome, on which a Territorial air squadron was encamped. Besides examining Wapitis, Avro trainers and a Hawker Hart belonging to the squadron, I was able to see over *Hannibal*, the new Handley-Page Imperial Airways machine, and have a look at an Air Union French machine and a big Fokker monoplane. There were also three private Puss Moths, and I was taken for a flight in a Puss Moth through clouds which bumped us about a good deal, and was taken on a Puss Moth formation flight which was a curious dream-like experience—seeing my neighbours' faces so close to me pressed against their window-panes, while below the ground dropped suddenly to Romney Marsh and the sea flowed thinly over the sands at low tide, scarcely discernible, through the channel haze. I also flew an ordinary Moth from the front cockpit, but I knew the pilot in the back must dislike it, and I did not even do a steep turn.

On Thursday I was gossiping on the aerodrome

after lunch, when a cry went up, and the medical officer on duty, to whom I had been talking, dashed off leaving me his dog to hold.

A crash—but where? I peered in all directions, but soon heard that the damaged machine was still in the air. The pilot, practising landing on a mark, had smashed his under-carriage and had taken off again at once. When he came round next time he found the ambulance and the fire-engine had been rushed out into conspicuous positions, and that the ground officer was waving him on, so he flew off to consider it. As he passed by, twenty feet above the ground, I saw the under-carriage wobbling like a loose tooth. The pilot's feelings when he realised the significance of the fire-engine I know nothing of, but on the ground our feelings were acute. Every man in the camp, every scullion and cook, fitter and rigger, appeared suddenly on the aerodrome, and nothing could have made any one of us turn our heads away.

The dog strained at his leash, and I stood motionless and paralysed. I suppose that mixture of disgust, curiosity and fear was the emotion called dread. But whatever was its name it was unwholesome and ignoble—a revelation of indecency. The dog strained and jumped at his leash, throttling himself to join his master, and I stood straining my eyes, watching and waiting to see men burn.

Damn you, dog. Lie down, you brute! The office clerks of the aerodrome had joined the cooks and scullions. The amphitheatre was packed. The show was free.

Meanwhile, the pilot had climbed up to 6000 feet or so to think things out and we had lost sight of him. And while they were making up their minds I held the dog and exorcised the indecency of waiting by making up my mind. What should I do? I did not remember that the Air Force all wear parachutes, or the problem would have been solved. I should without hesitation have joined the caterpillar club. But not knowing of the parachutes, my decision was to fly off to the seashore and alight in the sea where it was about four feet deep. One might turn upside down and drown, but one wouldn't burn. But presently the machine came gliding down silently from a great height, and on the aerodrome we became aware that this machine was the one for which we were all waiting. Emotion grew intense, saliva flowed in some mouths, while others' throats were parched and dry. And over the trees floated the machine inexorably while we twitched and the infernal dog whined and pulled. What a lovely slow glide! My God, the machine had touched the earth and was running forward. But when it had gone ten yards, it skidded and, as we stared, it reared up slowly on its nose. Have you watched and listened while the last cracks tear through the heartwood and the vast tree shivers and plunges slowly to its doom?

Just so slowly the machine balanced, plunged and went over on to its back, shivered and lay still. It did not catch fire. Neither of the occupants was seriously hurt, and a quarter of an hour after the ambulance and the fire-engine had raced up to the wreckage, the pilot went up again in another machine.

As soon as it was all over a charming lady appeared. 'Did you really see it all? I missed it. I'm always unlucky. The poor firemen! I've been talking to them. They've stood by on duty every afternoon and have never been called out before—and all for nothing.'

I thought I had never heard prettier sympathy for the poor lion without a Christian.

THIRD SOLO

AUGUST 13TH

After such thrills it was good to be back in the cockpit of *YZ*.

When I had made one or two circuits, I dropped Marshall and went off alone. There was no wind and I flew very badly, but in spite of everything, put her down five or six times quite safely.

SIDE-SLIPPING IN

AUGUST 19TH

The weather has broken again; the weathercock on the dovehouse was swinging wildly. It was too rough for me to practise landings and I went up with Marshall to do figures of eight. I took the machine up and began fighting the tilting tip-up wind and Marshall did a figure of eight round the marks used in the test. It was necessary to go well beyond each of the marks, and to keep some way away from them: directly the machine banked the wind swept it down on the point round which one was turning. Thus every turn began with a wide slow bank and finished with an almost vertical one as the wind swept us past. Naturally, when I began to do this I did not allow enough for the wind and was swept over the rifle butt which I should have gone round. This sort of flying was wildly exciting after the endless repetition of my circus-pony circuits. The drift of the wind was terrific, and then when I had got round I tried in vain to tighten the loop of the eight just enough with a vertical bank down wind and the speed over the ground changed wildly.

'Take her up now,' said Marshall. At 2000 he demonstrated side-slips. The sky was full of clouds but one could see a very long way.

'Shut the throttle. Start your bank, put on opposite rudder and bring the stick back as you slip and hold your bank on. To come out put the stick a little forward and centralise the controls.'

There was a real psychological difficulty in putting on opposite rudder, for stick and rudder seem to go together now. But the blast of air on the side of my face meant that all was well. The side-slips were beautiful with the cornfields rushing up as one looked over the side. I climbed again and looked with hawk's eyes (I haven't hawk's eyes, alas!) for Ray and the children 2000 feet below. No, they had not come yet. And once more we

came down side-slipping in a lovely grand chain—
to the left, to the right—down to the golden corn.
Then I brought the machine round high up, overshooting because of the wind. At the last moment I
saw she was drifting, and round we went again
while I yelled explanations down the tube. This
time the wind took off the extra height just as
planned and with an almost dead machine made
a perfect three-pointer. We ran ten yards at most.

'That was first-class,' said Marshall. 'You're
getting on now.'

FIGURES OF EIGHT

AUGUST 26TH

I had a wonderful romp in the air to-day and
passed my first test. The weather was lovely. The
sky was blue, the sun shone, one could see for miles.
While the barograph was being fetched, I did some
circuits and then getting bored, began doing figures
of eight. I did some perfect ones round the farther
mark, but round the nearer one they weren't so
good. Then I landed, the observer came out, the
barograph was stowed in behind. I took off. 'Not
too high now,' I remembered when I was already
nearly 300 feet up. Just as I reached the aerodrome
on my first figure of eight, I saw Ray drive up. I was
keeping the nose of the machine well down and had
no difficulty at all about height: for the whole time
I flew at about 250 feet. My turns round the rifle
butt were good.

While I tightened the turn I saw a group of bare-legged children below me with fishing-rods and looking up, so I stuck out an arm and waved. But my turns at the hangar end where I was being more closely watched were rather poor, perhaps because they were right-hand ones, and I have so much more practice with left-hand turns.

I did six figures of eight, then went off a little way, climbed a trifle, remembered the barograph, turned in and made an approach and glide. I came in too fast, a trifle too high, there was a slight bounce, but, damn it all, that would do.

'Well, I've passed my first test and feel quite cock-a-hoop. It was intoxicating doing those low turns.'

'I thought it must be very boring flying to and fro like that,' said Ray. 'I couldn't imagine why you were doing it.'

CLOUDS

MONDAY, AUGUST 31ST

There was a north wind dropping—a cloudy sky clearing, white clouds at 2000 feet and blue sky between. I went twice round with Marshall and then went off alone. After a few circuits, I flew off and started climbing. At 1500 feet I began to run into a cloud and went on through it. In a moment all was lost to sight. What a thrill when one's alone! 'Which way up am I? Could there be any doubt? Really it's rather silly to do this, isn't it?

Who knows, cloud banks might cut me off.' But I knew, of course, that there was fifteen hundred feet between the clouds and the earth. The white fluff faded: I was out in the blue. 'Now for a side-slip.' But my side-slip was a fiasco as the nose swung round. When I pulled out I was below the cloud and feeling slightly shaken. Gliding slowly, I picked out the aerodrome and descended but undershot a bit and had to give a spasm of engine to get in. Next time I went up I was wiser and looked about for a hole in the clouds to go through and swung about to dodge them. At 2800 I shut the throttle and side-slipped. Left bank and right rudder. The wind rushed at me, I slid forward in my seat against the belt, then centred the controls and put the stick forward and was out in a glide. Stick to the right and left rudder wasn't quite so successful, as I saw the prop. slow up till it was almost stopping, so I flicked the throttle open a little as I came out into the glide.

I have no ambitions to experiment with real forced landings. A right-hand side-slip slows up the propeller and one has to watch it. Marshall had told me, but I had forgotten and I had just rediscovered this truth for myself. The left slip was easy. I did another right-hand slip and watched the prop. slowing up and came in and landed. Then once more off, and up to 3000 feet. It was the first time that I had been alone with the clouds. They come fast: the whiteness darkens a little: the machine bumps: the engine sounds a little different, looking down one is grateful to

a patch of earth for being there. The blue breaks
and the clouds huddle below one, pierced by a
far landscape of fields and cornstooks. The white
Angora rabbits' fleeciness is fascinating.

THE HEIGHT TEST

SEPTEMBER 10TH

I had my medical examination and then went
to the aerodrome and was sent up alone without
the preliminary circuit. I went up to 2000 feet, and
did a rehearsal of my height test, gliding to and fro,
to and fro. By that time Hart had turned up and the
barograph was ready; it was stuck in behind and
off I flew and climbed to 4000, at which I shut the
throttle and glided down. It was cold up there or
I should have gone higher. I kept the machine
at a steady 60, turning her carefully well to the
south of the aerodrome and coming closer as I
came lower, and then just at the right height I
turned in, crossed the hedge and landed exquisitely. I had passed the test all right. No one
could have done it better. But to my disgust the
wretched barograph was insufficiently inked; it
had left off recording at 4000 feet up. 'I'll do
another.' And while the paper was being changed
I did a circuit. Then laden with the barograph
I went up again. This time the air seemed colder
still: it was ice-cold and I wriggled as low down
as I could in the cockpit. At 4000 I felt I had gone
as high as honour demanded, so I shut off and

glided down. Every thousand feet I gave a burst of engine to warm it up. Coming in I was a little high and a little close, and did a couple of wriggles and came in to a perfect landing. I just beat the wheels and the machine fell dead from a foot.

The barograph was pretty too.

MORE SOLO

SEPTEMBER 11TH

I went up alone and did fifty minutes climbing and side-slipping.

I like the air best above 2000 when one soars in circles. There is not the slightest doubt that big birds of prey which spend their lives wheeling about the sky at great heights have the happiest lives. My last landing was the worst that I have done for a long time. I overshot; the ground slopes downhill and I drifted far across without allowing for the ground sloping away. The result was a heavy drop.

THE RULES

SEPTEMBER 12TH

I went in and had my oral examination from Hart. Last night I read and re-read Leeming's book until I could answer every question, and this morning refreshed my memory. The result was that I was packed with information and answered every question. My paper was marked 100% answered correctly.

SOLO CROSS-COUNTRY

NOVEMBER 1ST

I have done a lot of flying since I got my A licence and have altogether some ten hours' solo to my credit, besides which I have done two cross-country flights with Marshall, flying by map and compass.

To fly cross-country by map, you first spread out your map and rule a straight line to the place to which you wish to fly. You then take a protractor and measure the angle between your course and the true north (always measuring the angle clockwise). You then add the magnetic variation of 12°, climb map in hand into the cockpit and set your compass. The top of it is movable and marked out into 360°. You unlock it and twist it around. You set it so that the point of the compass rim nearest to the engine reads the number of degrees at which your course lies to the magnetic north. After which you have only to fly keeping your north needle pointing to the fixed N of the compass rim. The map you stow in the pigeon-hole in the dash and pull out when you are in the air to hold in the left hand. Thereafter you have only to correct your compass course by picking up and identifying places on the map.

In decent weather this isn't difficult in a country

like England where there are a great many obvious
features, such as railways.

To-day I went for my first solo cross-country to
Hunstanton and back. There was a S.W. wind and
a pearly grey sky. But just before I took off, Marshall pointed out that I was setting my compass
wrong. I had left out the 12° of magnetic variation!

Once I was off I turned in a circuit and slowly
climbed to 2000. The air was hazy. I could not
see far ahead, but below and to one side was quite
clear. Soon I pulled out my first map and looked
to see the windmill at Stretham. I was directly
on my course. Ely was very clear, with the great
cathedral running east and west. Beyond it was
water gleaming, and very soon the two parallel
Bedford cuts with the Wash between them. As I
flew, I kept picking out fields in which to make
forced landings, green pastures or dun stubble
between the black newly ploughed fen land. At
intervals I glanced at the oil pressure and r.p.m.

The country unrolled itself more clearly. The
Bedford level ended and flowed into winding loops
crossed by the three Wiggenhall bridges. Beyond, a
great smoke rose from some factory, and the smoke
of King's Lynn spread beyond. I gazed down at
the strange and familiar geography of a town one
knows. The gatehouse, the market by the church,
the big market and the docks were familiar enough.
But the big park and the railway sidings were a
surprise. The estuary of the river ran straight and
free towards the Wash.

Grey, the drossy grey of leaden mud, the pearlier

shallow waters which vanished into the mist, that
was the Wash. A haze clung over the water. Soon
I was at Heacham, where the broader sands had
contracted into a narrow belt and bungalows
clustered and a branch of railway curved away
inland. A tug was setting out from Hunstanton
jetty. Beyond, the sea was visible and the line of
the coast curved round. I could see the whole
sweep of the Norfolk coast as far perhaps as Wells-
next-the-Sea. True, it was only the Wash beneath
me, but I was flying over salt water. It was the
sea. If I kept straight on I should get the greater
part of the 500 miles to Norway before I ran out
of petrol and drowned.

If I swung round due east I might get easily to
Holland before it was exhausted. But one cannot
do that sort of thing on impulse, and when I was
about 500 yards off Hunstanton pier, I swirled
round in my tracks in a vertical bank. Before me
I could see the pearl-grey water netted with tiny
ripples, the yellow sands, and ahead of me the
sunshine falling dimly through the mussel-shell
slate mother-of-pearl mist, thickened here and
there in curdled spots of white cloud. To my left
were the trees and warrens of Sandringham, to
my right rippled the grey waters with haze and
sandbanks. The mouth of the Ouse ran like a bar
of silver through the wriggling mudflats to King's
Lynn. As I passed over the town, flying almost
directly into the sun, the distant cuts, drains,
dykes, waterways and rivers gleamed high up,
suddenly startling me with the dazzle of ghostly

silver Zeppelins on my own level in the air. I was
flying just below the clouds, and when I reached
the Bedford River I pressed back the stick to go up
through them. Clouds cloaked me in shapelessness,
the machine bumped gently, I opened the throttle
a trifle as the r.p.m. fell off a little, shreds of
vapour passed by me and the sun shone more
radiant and more golden. At 3000 I was above the
plain of vapour. The sun shone brilliantly, black
shadows of struts and wires striped my wings. On
my left a vast area of milk was ruffled here and there
with white-cap breakers. A wall of skimmed milk
stretched facing me across the sky. But on my right
the milky sea was calm: no cloud clotted, with
curdled white, the almost transparent whey. Yet
even that sea was not absolutely uniform, but
watered and laced with long, low, gentle waves
that divided the pacific calm. I was alone, and a
happy forgetfulness came over me as I gazed at
this mood of Nature's.

Plane, engine, oil and air-speed were forgotten,
as a car is forgotten, and at 5000 feet I floated in
a soundless disembodied dream, waking occasionally, it is true, to put my head into the cockpit and
peer blindly until my sun-dazzled eyes could make
the compass out. I was on my course—and there on
my left was Ely and before me—rising up as high
as my own level—the sunlit loops of the Cam, somewhere near Cambridge, seen sparkling through the
bank of pearl-grey mist. I had laid the maps aside
long since, but when I saw on my right some
pans of water, I shut the throttle and glided down.

The glittering squares were the sewage farm and Cambridge was invisible but near. The machine bumped as I passed through cloud. The air-speed fell to 60 as I glided slowly down. Yes, there before me were the hangars and the aerodrome. I did a big side-slip, but even so I overshot and went round again. This time my approach was perfect and my landing curiously soft and dreamlike. I was on the earth, but the earth was unreal: a limbo of haze and softened sunlight. Reality was far above me. There were no shadows here on earth and scarcely any sounds except that my ear squeaked suddenly as the air rushed into the eustachian tube.

.   .   .   .   .   .

As I drove I saw the sunset on my left, and pulled up for a moment to look at pencils of grey, needles of fire, floating in the blue-green lake transparency, high and far above the stubble fields. I saw there the last visible moments of that other mood of Nature's and I felt it beckoning . . . beckoning.

I MAY not ever have the aeroplane of which I dream, my own 'plane which will be stowed away in a lonely barn between a hay-tedder and a horse-rake. When I do own it I shall neglect it for weeks at a time, but then one morning when there are big white clouds and the spring air is soft, I shall walk across the fields and unlock the barn door and there the 'plane will be, waiting for me. As I edge round it, a brown hen will fly up cackling from her clutch of eggs in the cockpit and I shall chase her away angrily. There will be a thick layer of hay dust over everything, sparrows will have dropped straws from their nests and have made messes on the wings.

I shall prop open the double doors and lifting the machine by the tail push her out into the sunlight to look her over carefully. Then I shall swing out the wings and lock them, unhook and fold away the jury-struts and kick the chocks into place under the wheels. Then, after flooding the carburettor, turn the prop. over once or twice to suck in, switch on, and seizing the propeller blade, give her one good swing.

As I jolt along, taxying out into the sixteen acre field, I shall be all alone. There will be no one within sight, not one living thing to watch me and nothing in the sky except a lark or two. And then, when I've strapped myself in and turned into wind, I shall take-off alone and unobserved into the empty sky.

That is still a dream, and unless it comes true I shall go on, all my life hanging about an aerodrome, flying school machines when I can afford to, gossiping with the ground engineer, and finding pleasure merely in looking at aeroplanes and in watching other people land. I think even if I were to go blind I should still go to the aerodrome for the sound of a machine landing thrills me. That bucketing hollow noise that dies into a rumble: as though an empty barrel were bouncing down three stairs and tittupping to rest: Gosh, it is the most exciting sound I know.

There she turns on the ground; she is coming in. Pull on your helmet. You're next.

THE END

1101457R0

Printed in Great Britain by
Amazon.co.uk, Ltd.,
Marston Gate.